W9-BKA-820

African Village Folktales

Books written and illustrated by Edna Mason Kaula

AFRICAN VILLAGE FOLKTALES

LEADERS OF THE NEW AFRICA

Edna Mason Kaula

AFRICAN
VILLAGE
FOLKTALES

Illustrated by the Author

THE WORLD PUBLISHING COMPANY/CLEVELAND AND NEW YORK

Published by The World Publishing Company
2231 West 110th Street, Cleveland, Ohio 44102
Published simultaneously in Canada by
Nelson, Foster & Scott Ltd.
Library of Congress catalog card number: 68–14690
Designed by Jack Jaget

ACKNOWLEDGMENT

The author and the publisher extend their gratitude to The Clarendon Press, England, for their permission to retell the story "The Caterpillar and the Wild Animals" from the *Masai— Their Language and Folklore,* by Sir Claud Hollis, and to Simon and Schuster, New York, for their permission to use material based on a Pygmy story from *The Forest People,* copyright 1961 by Colin M. Turnbull.

Among Africa's children
to whom this book is dedicated
are Kulame, Mpunzi, and Ptebe,
who retold tales they had
"learned by listening," and to
Joseph Ndandarika who has captured
the moods of Africa's animals
in sculptured stone and wood.

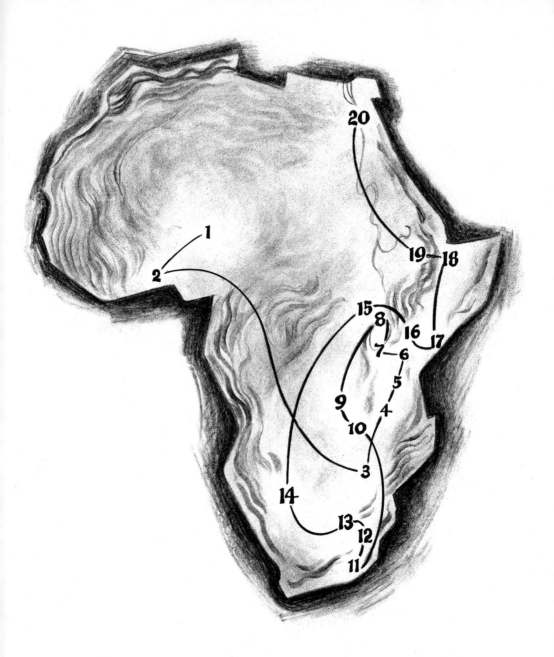

By matching the numbers on the map with the numbers of the stories in the table of contents you will see where in Africa the storytellers live.

Contents

INTRODUCTION   15

1. WARTHOG AND HORNBILL   19

   A STORY FROM THE HAUSA PEOPLE

2. ANANSE AND HIS VISITOR, TURTLE   25

   A STORY FROM THE ASHANTI PEOPLE

3. KALULU AND HIS MONEY FARM   32

   A STORY FROM THE MASHONA PEOPLE

4. LION AND HONEY BADGER   43

   A STORY FROM THE NYAKYUSA PEOPLE

5. LION, CHAMELEON, AND CHICKEN   49

    A STORY FROM THE GOGO PEOPLE

6. THE RAIN MAKERS   55

    A STORY FROM THE CHAGGA PEOPLE

7. HOW FROG LOST HIS TAIL   60

    A STORY FROM THE SUKUMA PEOPLE

8. HOW CHAMELEON BECAME KING
    OF THE ANIMALS   65

    A STORY FROM THE BAGANDA PEOPLE

9. THE TUG OF WAR   71

    A STORY FROM THE BALUBA PEOPLE

10. THE PATTERN ON TORTOISE'S BACK   77

    A STORY FROM THE BEMBA PEOPLE

11. HOW ANIMALS GOT THEIR
    BEAUTIFUL COATS   84

    A STORY FROM THE ZULU PEOPLE

12. THE INJURED LION   91

    A STORY FROM THE SWAZI PEOPLE

13. IN UNITY IS STRENGTH   96

    A STORY FROM THE BAVENDA PEOPLE

14. THE BATTLE OF THE ANIMALS   101

    A STORY FROM THE BUSHMAN PEOPLE

15. THE BIRD WITH THE MOST
    BEAUTIFUL SONG   110

    A STORY FROM THE PYGMY PEOPLE

16. THE MIGHTY WARRIOR IN HARE'S
    HOUSE   118

    A STORY FROM THE MASAI PEOPLE

17. A LOT OF SILENCE MAKES A GREAT
    NOISE   126

    A STORY FROM THE SWAHILI PEOPLE

18. THE LIGHT IN THE HOUSE   133

    A STORY FROM THE GALLA PEOPLE

19. LION AND THE WOMAN   139

    A STORY FROM THE AMHARA PEOPLE

20. THE WISE OLD CAMEL   146

    A STORY FROM THE EGYPTIAN PEOPLE

THE END OF THE EVENING   155

Introduction

At one time we thought of Africa only as a mysterious continent, teeming with ferocious animals and unfriendly people. Then the fascination of the unknown lured adventurous explorers who crossed the continent from north to south and from east to west, uncovering Africa's secrets and recounting the magic of their discoveries for all the world to hear. Today we read about the new African nations, about their leaders and their people, who share with the rest of the world the great march into the future.

But Africa's literature waits for further exploration. It is a rich and vital art form that influenced the shaping of Africa's social patterns. African village folktales are still more often told than written, but in the telling and the retelling they help to preserve a harmony and a unity in village life that have no equal anywhere. Storytelling time brings together all the members of the village—young and old—to share a common heritage.

In the olden days in Africa there were no written languages to aid in teaching boys and girls. Even today there are many places far out in the country where children learn only by listening. Their fathers teach them family and tribal history in story form; their mothers ask them riddles to sharpen their wits.

The best place for learning is around the open fire at night. Every village, no matter how small, has its storyteller. "Come listen to my story," he calls. The villagers—men, women, and children—answer, "We come, we listen, we learn."

A clever storyteller acts out the story as he tells it. He imitates the noises animals make—hissing like Snake, roaring like Lion. Children in the audience sit spellbound. Sometimes they join in, hissing and roaring with him.

The storyteller repeats tales and legends about both good and bad spirits. He explains beginnings—how the moon was made, and the stars, and the earth. His memory holds stories of life and love and death, most of them stressing strong moral lessons. Although every tribal area has its own stories, today many old stories are told and retold throughout Africa in varying forms and in different languages.

Perhaps African children enjoy best of all hearing tales of animals that behave like human beings. Here are twenty such stories, learned by listening in the villages of West, Central, East, and southern Africa.

African Village Folktales

1. Warthog and Hornbill

A STORY FROM THE HAUSA PEOPLE

The People

The sinking sun resembles an enormous, flame-edged flower when it drops into the Atlantic Ocean beyond the bulge that is West Africa. In its daylong journey from the east, the sun has cast its light on mountains and swamplands, on arid deserts and rain forests, and on wide grassy expanses called savannas. It has shone on countless tribes speaking different languages and practicing different customs. The peoples of West Africa are as diversified as their land, but they have in common a cherished store of legends and folktales.

Nigeria is West Africa's largest nation, and of Nigeria's many tribes the Hausa group is by far the largest. They occupy the land in northern Nigeria and claim to have come originally from Mecca, the holy city of the Moslems. In their villages, the Hausas build square houses of sun-

19

baked bricks, covered with plaster on which the village artists draw colorful designs—of animals or people or geometric figures. For coolness, the flat roofs are covered with mud, spread over the wooden beams like chocolate frosting on a cake. Should swallows choose to nest under the roof of a new house the owner rejoices, for swallows are thought to bring good luck.

Donkeys and camels move at a slow deliberate pace from one Hausa village to the next, or from the fields where the peanut crops are stored in burlap sacks. The older boys help their fathers pile the sacks into pyramids twenty feet high to await shipment to countries beyond Nigeria. Both the boys and their fathers wear full-flowing cotton robes, usually white, and round flat caps upon their heads, which is a Moslem custom.

Girls, like their mothers, wear long cotton garments fastened under their arms and bright-colored turbans gracefully arranged over their tightly braided hair. Together they pick the cotton bolls, then spin the cotton into yarn which the men weave into cloth. Small children wear few clothes; a short waistband perhaps, and strings of beads. Little boys have their heads shaved except for a narrow fringe across the back or a pointed tuft on top.

The Moslems were the first to bring a written language into West Africa. In school, Hausa children study from small wooden boards that are carved or painted with the symbols of their language. They clasp a handle that protrudes from the top of the board and follow the symbols with the middle finger of the right hand.

Children put aside their boards and join the other vil-

lagers when the storyteller calls. If he has made a pilgrimage to Mecca the storyteller wears a green turban and is called Hadji, an honored title. He prefers stories that will explain the origin of important Moslem laws. Nobody knows who wrote them or how much they have changed through centuries of retelling.

The members of the audience are curious as to what lesson they will hear. Many chew on kola nuts—a stimulat-

ing fruit that satisfies hunger and quenches thirst. The moist fragrance of night comes on; a puff of wind clears the smoke from the fire. The storyteller holds his chilled hands to the flame and then, reclining on a straw mat, begins his story.

The Story

One day a Moslem nobleman and his attendants became lost while riding through the forest. They grew weak from thirst. When the nobleman saw Hornbill sleeping on a branch overhead, he stopped.

"Pardon me, Hornbill, but can you tell me where we can find water?" he called.

But Hornbill, being a lazy selfish bird, merely opened one eye, puffed out his feathers, and clacked, "I don't know," with his outsize beak.

The nobleman and his men rode wearily on. Presently they came upon Mrs. Warthog who was busy digging up roots for her family's supper.

The nobleman raised his voice above the noisy snuffling and wuffling around the tree. "Pardon me, Mrs. Warthog, but can you tell me where we can find water?" he shouted.

The Warthog family looked up at once. Although Mrs. Warthog was undoubtedly the ugliest animal in Africa, with big fleshy bumps all over her mud-covered face, the horsemen could tell that she had a tender heart as she smiled up at them from under her bristly eyelashes.

"I shall be happy to lead so distinguished a traveler to water," she replied in a gravelly sort of voice. She set off at a fast trot with her three young ones, who held their spindly tails straight up, in single file behind her. Mrs. Warthog led the tired travelers through the woods, then over a hill, and into a ravine. She left them to satisfy their thirst from a deep clear pool that lay in a rocky hollow.

The men drank; the horses drank. When they were refreshed, the nobleman raised his arms and spoke to the sky. "From now until the end of time, Hornbill shall drink but once every third day," he announced in a deep voice. "And to protect Warthog the law shall be that Moslems must never eat the flesh of pigs."

To this day, hornbills are seldom seen drinking and Moslems who follow their religion closely refrain from eating pork or ham.

2. Ananse and His Visitor, Turtle

A STORY FROM THE ASHANTI PEOPLE

The People

Listeners hear the story of Warthog and Hornbill around every fire in every village where there are Africans who follow the Moslem religion: along Nigeria's seacoast on the Gulf of Guinea, where more pure Negroid people live than anywhere else in Africa; in Ghana, where the Ashanti live; and in the rest of Africa.

In Ghana, those Ashanti who live in villages build small round houses consisting of a framework of slender poles covered with woven grass reeds. Boys and girls help to thatch the little houses with sheaves of grass cut in short lengths. They overlap the sheaves so that the thatching keeps out the rain. Inside the houses there are mats for sleeping and perhaps a few stools, but no other furniture.

Even when they are very young, girls help their mothers mold clay jars for use in cooking, which is done outdoors or in a special building. As they grow older they learn to carry jars or trays laden with fruit upon their heads. Boys learn to gather the huge, yellow cacao pods that grow from the tree trunks. They crack the pods open, to get at the cacao beans that make delicious chocolate and cocoa.

West Africans of past days created magnificent bronze statues and wooden masks that were far superior to any other art south of the Sahara. Today some young people are trained to be sculptors and painters, others to be musicians. They are taught to play musical instruments that are found nowhere else but in West Africa. They rap smart rat-tat-tats on rhythm drums so fast that one cannot see the movement of their hands. They send messages on beautifully carved hollow logs to far-off villages. When villagers hear the call to "hurry, hurry—hear a story," crowds form a circle around the community fire.

West Africa is rich in the number and variety of its stories. The folktales of the Ashanti tribe are particularly noted for their humor. It was the Ashanti who created a group of tales about Ananse, a cunning spider that tries to outwit his neighbors. He seldom succeeds.

The Story

It was almost time for Sun to sink to his resting place when Turtle, tired and dusty from hours of wandering, came to Ananse's house in the middle of a clearing in the woods. Turtle was hungry and the appetizing aroma of freshly cooked fish and yams drew him to approach

26

Ananse's door and to knock. Ananse jerked the door open. When he saw the tired stranger he was inwardly annoyed, but it was an unwritten law of his country, that one must never, no never, refuse hospitality to a passer-by.

Ananse smiled grimly and said, "Come in, come in, and share my dinner, Mr. Turtle."

As Turtle stretched out one paw to help himself from the steaming platter Ananse almost choked on a mouthful of food. In a shocked voice he said, "Turtle, I must remind you that in my country it is ill-mannered to come to the table without first washing. Please go to the stream at the foot of the hill and wash your dusty paws."

Turtle waddled down the hill and waded in the water for a while. He even washed his face. By the time he had trudged back up the trail to Ananse's house, the platter of fish was half empty. Ananse was eating at a furious rate.

Turtle stretched out one paw to help himself to food, but again Ananse stopped him. "Turtle, your paws are still dusty. Please, go wash them."

"It is the dust from the long trail up the hill," Turtle explained in a meek voice. Clearly, it was not Turtle's place to argue if he expected to share the delectable meal, so he crawled down the hill a second time and rewashed his paws. Turtle was careful to walk on the grass beside the dusty trail on the climb back to Ananse's house. He hurried, for by now he was ravenous.

But, oh dear! Ananse had scraped the platter bare of fish and yams. "My, that was a good dinner," he said, wiping the last drop of gravy from his chin.

28

"Thank you for your wonderful hospitality, Ananse. Some day you must visit me." And Turtle, in a huff, went on home.

Some months later Ananse visited Turtle. After creepy crawling all day from one tall grass stem to the next he found Turtle snoozing beside the river.

"Well, well," exclaimed Turtle. "So you have come to share my dinner. Make yourself comfortable, my dear Ananse, while I go below and prepare the food." He plunged into the river with a splash. Ananse was hungry. He paced the shore line and watched for Turtle's reappearance.

At last Turtle's head popped above the water. "Dinner is ready," he called as he bit into a huge clam. "Come on down." Then he disappeared from sight.

Ananse dived head first into the water, sank a few inches, then floated to the surface. His spindly legs and tiny body prevented him from sinking. He flipped and flapped his puny arms, tried swallow dives and belly flops, but he could not reach the bed of the river.

Then that cunning spider schemed. He filled the pockets of his jacket with small round pebbles, dived into the river, and sank with a bump that landed him right at the dinner table. Before him was spread the most delicious meal he had ever seen. There were oysters and clams, mussels, slices of eel, and crabs. As a centerpiece, sprays of watercress rested against large pink shrimp. Ananse's eyes widened with pleasure, his stomach rumbled in anticipation.

Turtle, already seated at the table, swallowed a piece of

eel, looked at Ananse and said, "Oh, Ananse, I must remind you that in my country it is ill-mannered to come to the table wearing a jacket. Please take it off."

Very slowly Ananse removed his jacket. Very slowly Ananse left the table. Without the weight of the pebbles to hold him down he floated straight up through the green water and out of sight.

When you set out to outsmart another person to your own advantage, there is usually someone who can outsmart you.

3. Kalulu and His Money Farm

A STORY FROM THE MASHONA PEOPLE

The People

Ananse the Spider is an invention of the Ashanti tribe of
West Africa. Kalulu the Hare is an invention of the Bantu

people who live almost everywhere below the equator, and just a little bit above the equator. Kalulu, though not as cunning as Ananse, is a big know-it-all. In the tales about Kalulu that the storytellers of hundreds of Bantu tribes repeat, he is usually advising or scolding, trying to be an important person.

Bantu villages are generally made up of families whose members are related to one another, though there are a few exceptions. Some villages contain a dozen small round huts, other villages contain hundreds of huts under a chief.

When village boys are about seven years old they learn to take care of the sheep and goats, then when they are about twelve years old they rise to the position of herd-boys. If they live in Central Africa, they spend their days

when they are not in school following the cattle on the savannas and veld. Or among the beautiful hills and valleys if they live in southern Africa. The boys drive the cattle back to the villages at the end of each day and shut them in an enclosure called a cattle kraal. Sometimes the kraal is surrounded by a thornbush fence as a protection from wild animals.

Among the Mashona Bantu tribes of Rhodesia, boys learn from their fathers how to cut the poles for the framework of a new hut and how to bind the long grass into sheaves for the cone-shaped roof. Girls help their mothers grind up the hard soil from anthills that sometimes rise to heights of twenty feet. The hills are built by the ants when they clear the ground for their nests deep in the earth. The ants add a secretion to the discarded soil which causes it to become almost as hard as cement. The Mashona women mix water and clay with the powdered anthill soil and then spread this mixture on the inside wall and over the floor of a new hut. When the mixture dries it hardens again. Then the women and the girls rub the floor with a round stone until it shines as brightly as sunlight on a quiet forest pool.

The Mashona people are farmers as well as herders, for girls also learn how to plant seeds. First they make small holes in the earth with pointed sticks. Then, from a mouthful of seeds, they spit out one seed to a hole as they move between the rows. After the planting, the tribal chief blesses the fields to insure a good harvest.

As day closes smoke spirals before each hut as fires are lighted. The cattle are in their kraals, and when the villagers finish their supper, often a stew made rich and savory with herbs gathered from the veld, it is storytelling time.

Mothers, fathers, great aunts, uncles, and all the children in the village squeeze into the widening circle to hear an old story, invented when cowrie shells were used as money.

The Story

One planting time, just before the seasonal rains started, the chief ordered each animal to grow one certain crop. He told Warthog to grow the yams, Baboon the corn, Elephant the sorghum, and so on. But Kalulu the Hare, the big show-off, spoke up and said:

"Chief, give me a bag of money and I will grow such a large crop that you will be rich."

"Nonsense," boomed the chief. "No one can grow cowrie shells."

Kalulu leaned close to the chief's ear. "I have the secret," he whispered knowingly.

The chief trusted Kalulu. He gave him a bag of cowrie shells. Of course, Kalulu had no intention of trying to grow money. He bought new clothes, fancy tidbits for his dinner, furnishings for his home, and strings of shiny beads for Mrs. Hare. Kalulu thought he was smart. He forgot the awful consequences that would follow, when his mischief would be discovered.

"Where is the money you promised to grow?" asked the chief at harvest time.

35

"Money is a very slow-growing crop, Chief. Perhaps it will be ready next year." Kalulu still felt confident and was excited by all the luxuries he had bought.

Next year—and the next—Kalulu gave the same answer. At last the chief ordered Warthog, a most dependable animal, to go with Kalulu to his money garden. For the first time Kalulu was afraid. How could he prevent Warthog from learning the dreadful truth!

"Oh, Warthog," Kalulu pleaded in a pained voice. "Not today, please. I have a bad case of indigestion. The garden is miles from here—deep in the forest. Have pity on a poor sick hare, Warthog."

"The chief ordered me to visit your garden, Kalulu, and visit it I will. We'll walk slowly and the fresh air will be good for you."

Kalulu, brooding and sullen, led the way into the cool green forest. Warthog, determined, followed. Vines hung from the trees. Ferns crowded the trail. The woods were very quiet.

Kalulu was quiet also, trying to plot a means of escape. He stopped suddenly. "Warthog," he said. "We'll have to sleep in the garden tonight. I must go back for my pillow, but you wait here."

Kalulu went back over the trail, looked for a long, hollow reed, found one, and from it cut a hunter's horn. He crept through the bushes until he came level with Warthog. Kalulu put the horn to his lips, blew a blast, and shouted in a gruff voice, "Hunters, hunters! I see a fat Warthog—come catch him for supper."

"Who wants to be someone's supper?" grunted Wart-

36

hog. "Not I!" He scooted toward home as fast as his legs would carry him.

Kalulu was saved. He hurried to the chief and in a puzzled voice said, "When I returned with my pillow, Chief, something in the forest must have frightened Warthog for he was gone."

The chief then called on Lion to go with Kalulu. And inwardly, Kalulu trembled. How could he scare Lion who was the bravest, strongest, most fearless animal in Bantuland! He thought deeply as he led Lion along the narrow trail through the forest.

"Bother!" Kalulu said when they were deep in the woods. "I have forgotten my hoe. Wait here, Lion, while I run home for it."

"I'll take a nap in this spot of sun while I'm waiting," said Lion with a wide yawn that showed his long, strong teeth. He snuggled into the fork of a low-growing tree and at once fell asleep.

Kalulu was in a panic. He scarcely noticed that he had left the trail until he tripped over something large and bulky half hidden in the grass. "Bother," he said, struggling to his feet. Then he grinned. "What luck!"

Kalulu stooped and picked up a twisted antelope horn almost three feet long. It was the kind of horn from which his tribe made trumpets, their sound so loud that it shook the mountains.

"What luck!" Kalulu repeated as he carved a mouthpiece with his little knife a few inches from the narrow end of the horn.

Kalulu crept back to where Lion slept. He pushed the

trumpet through the bushes near Lion's ear, took a long breath, and blew. *Blarrh-rh-rh!* The noise rent the air, bent the bushes, and shook poor Lion from his untroubled sleep. He scrambled to his feet and dashed for home.

Kalulu, chuckling to himself and filled with self-importance, swaggered back to the village and reported to the chief. "When I returned from collecting my hoe, Chief, Lion was not there. Something in the forest must have frightened him."

"Surely not brave Lion!" gasped the chief.

Lion hung his head. "There are bad spirits in that forest, Chief," he said.

"Shame on you, Lion," the chief scolded. He stroked his chin. "Mmm . . . Warthog, who is known for his honesty, failed. Lion, who was known for his courage until

a recent event, failed." He studied each animal in turn. "Tortoise, you are known for your good sense. Make Kalulu lead you to his money farm. See that he harvests the crop. Bring it to me. Now, go!"

Kalulu, plodding along the forest trail, had a scary feeling that at last he had been trapped by his own silly stupid tricks. His knees trembled. He could hardly push one heavy foot before the other.

Tortoise followed at a slow even pace. He dropped the satchel he was carrying when Kalulu suddenly said, "You know, Tortoise, I've forgotten my pillow. You wait here, and I'll run home for it."

"You don't need to, Kalulu. You can use mine." Tortoise hauled a pink and white striped pillow from the satchel.

They plodded on. The forest was silent except for the sound of their steps scuffing through the dried leaves and the beat, beat, beat of Kalulu's heart.

"Bother," said Kalulu, stopping again. "I've forgotten my hoe. You wait here, Tortoise, and I'll run home for it."

"You don't need to Kalulu. You can use mine." Tortoise pulled a short-handled hoe from the satchel.

What could he do? What dreadful punishment would be his when the fraud was discovered? Perhaps he would be tossed into jail—or hanged. He might even be put into a pie! If he could find a way to escape he would never boast or brag again! Such were Kalulu's dismal thoughts as they walked on in silence.

For a third time, Kalulu stopped. "Lion was right, Tortoise," he said with a shiver. "There are bad spirits in this forest. I can hear them. Stay here and I'll run home for my charms."

"You don't need to, Kalulu. I have charms. Don't be a scared hare! That soft smooth sound like moaning spirits is Termite and his family munching the tree trunks."

"I say they're spirits. If you don't watch out, they'll get you. But they won't get me!"

Kalulu turned, raced home, flung open the door, and shouted to his wife, "Help me! Hide me! They know I cheated."

"About the money crop?" she asked.

"Yes, yes! Hide me quickly!"

"Where? How? There's nowhere."

"Pretend I am your baby, Wife. Pull out all my fur and cover me with clay. Now! At once!"

She did as he told her. It was a painful ordeal for Kalulu. Each time Mrs. Hare pulled out a handful of fur he squirmed and groaned.

"Hush! Be still!" she scolded. "You brought this on yourself, you know."

Kalulu was one third his normal size without his thick coat, and very pink—like a newborn hare. Mrs. Hare just had time to smear him with clay and sling him in a shawl across her back (the way all Bantu mothers carry their babies) when a sharp rap sounded on the door.

"We are the chief's warriors," growled the taller of two men who carried spears and shields. "Where is Kalulu?"

Mrs. Hare shrugged. "He is not here, sir. Maybe he's harvesting the crop on his money farm. Only Baby and I are home at present."

"Give me the child," the warrior demanded. "We will hold him as a hostage until Kalulu delivers his money crop."

Mrs. Hare protested, but the warriors insisted, so she rolled Kalulu in a blanket made from lambskin and placed him carefully in a basket. As she lowered the lid Mrs. Hare whispered, "In the morning when I bring breakfast pretend that you are dead." Then she tied the lid securely with a piece of string.

Next morning, when Mrs. Hare opened the basket, she uttered anguished cries and shrieks. There lay her "Baby," eyes closed, body stretched out stiffly, paws lying limply.

"My Baby, my Baby," she wailed. "You've killed my Baby." Mrs. Hare threw herself on the ground. Not even a cup of good, strong tea succeeded in stopping the flow of tears, the moans, the groans, the hysterical outbursts of crying.

The chief was a kind man—easily deceived, as we have already seen. He blamed himself for Mrs. Hare's tragedy. "There, there," he said, patting her on the shoulder. Mrs. Hare wept louder. The village women wept with her. Even the chief blinked away a few tears as he ordered a servant to bring the contents of his treasury.

"There is little we can do to ease your grief, Mrs. Hare, but please accept this bag of money as a tiny token of our sympathy."

Mrs. Hare hesitated long enough to be polite. Then she tucked the money bag under one arm, the basket under the other, faked a few more sobs, and went to her home.

She found Kalulu groaning with stiffness and shivering in his nakedness. "I'm cured of boasting and bragging and cheating; I promise never to do it again," he declared.

"See that you keep your promise," Mrs. Hare cautioned. Then she gave him a tender hug.

"When Kalulu had grown a new fur coat—long, thick, glossy, more luxuriant than ever—he took the bag of money and laid it before the chief. "At last, Chief, here is the crop of money I promised to grow for you."

The good chief was made happy, but no happier than Kalulu who had learned that lies and deceit bring only troubles and worries.

42

4. Lion and Honey Badger

A STORY FROM THE NYAKYUSA PEOPLE

The People

Nyakyusa Bantu people also enjoy Kalulu stories. Their villages nestle in the valleys among the mountains near Lake Malawi in southeast Africa. They are friendly and hospitable people who like to plant trees and flowers for beauty as well as for shade in their well-swept tidy villages. If you visited a village you would see that there are no boys older than ten or eleven years. At that age an important event takes place. Boys are sent from their parents' homes to set up villages of their own. At first, two or three boys build small square houses together on the edge of their parents' village. They learn to plant crops for their own use under a leader who is chosen from among them. Gradually the boy-villages grow in size. By the time the boys are old enough to marry their villages are of normal size.

For clothing, the Nyakyusa men and women wear short skirts made from the bark of young trees which has been hammered with an elephant tusk until it is soft. The chief feature of women's and girls' costumes are the wide copper and brass bands the metalworkers design for their waists, arms, and ankles.

Metalworkers also make the cowbells, which the cattle wear in strings around their necks. The bell tones and the sighing of the wind against the surrounding hills are background music during storytelling time, which is of course shared by the visitors from the boy-villages who always come back home to eat.

One Kalulu story must have originated during his period of reform, for in it Kalulu is a subdued and humble Hare. The tale is as popular with southern Tanzania and Malawi Bantu people as it is with the Nyakyusa.

45

The Story

A rare and surprising friendship sprang up between Lion and Honey Badger. Lion's home was in the tall grass on one side of a narrow valley. Honey Badger's home was in an old anthill on the other side of the valley.

Whenever Lion brought home a good-size piece of meat he called to his friend, "Come and share this nice piece of meat with me." Then Honey Badger wasted no time in trotting across the valley on his short bowed legs to share the feast his friend offered.

When Honey Badger found chunks of honeycomb after following Honey Bird to the wild beehives, he called out, "Extra large bit of honey today, Lion. Please come to dinner." Then Lion would lope across the valley to Honey Badger's burrow.

One day a stranger came to the valley. It was Kalulu. He was so eager to start housekeeping that he forgot to check his surroundings. He built his little house right in the middle of the valley between the homes of Honey Badger and Lion, where the grass grew the greenest.

Next time Honey Badger called out, "Extra nice honey. Come and share it with me," Kalulu heard him first. He answered, "No thank you. I don't like honey," and went on nibbling grass.

When Lion called, "A whole leg of antelope. Come and have some," Kalulu heard first. He answered, "No thank you. I don't like meat," and went on nibbling grass.

The two friends were puzzled. Next time they met, Honey Badger said, "Have I offended you, Lion, that you refuse to share my honey?"

Lion said, "I didn't hear you ask me. But what have I done that you refuse to share my meat?"

"I didn't hear you ask me," said Honey Badger. "But *you* said, 'I don't like honey.'"

"That's funny," said Lion. "*You* said, 'I don't like meat.' Let's investigate this mystery."

Lion and Honey Badger found Kalulu nibbling grass in the middle of the valley. "I'll gobble you up quick," growled Lion, pouncing.

"Just a minute," squeaked Kalulu, hopping aside and trying to look brave though his nose twitched with fear. "If you insist on gobbling me up, let it be where I choose."

"Oh, all right," said Lion. "Where?"

Kalulu led Lion and Honey Badger to a tremendous old heap of ashes. "Here," he shouted. Plunk, he landed in the powdery ashes. Up they spurted in every direction.

By the time Lion and Honey Badger wiped the ashes from their eyes Kalulu had sprinted out of sight.

Next time Kalulu built a house he remembered to check his surroundings carefully.

5. Lion, Chameleon, and Chicken

A STORY FROM THE GOGO PEOPLE

The People

Just a little to the north of where the Nyakyusa villages nestle among the mountains, lies Tanzania, a country where more than one hundred different Bantu tribes live. The Gogo Bantu are among the largest in number. They live on a wide central plain between lakes and the sea.

Gogo villages sometimes reflect the influence of Arab traders of past days. The square adobe houses are set in rows rather than in a circle, the usual practice in Africa to afford protection from predatory animals and enemies. The villagers paint the houses white and roof them with grass thatch. Goats and chickens outnumber cattle in the villages, for the plains are in a hot dry area, unsuitable for cattle-raising.

Older Gogo boys help in planting cassava and other crops. Girls learn from their mothers how to select the best

palm leaves for weaving. After splicing the leaves into long narrow strands, they dye them in brilliant colors then weave or braid the strands into traditional baskets or trays. The beautiful patterns they create have names one of which is *uhuru,* meaning "free." The Gogo women are known also for their pottery. When the clay pots they make are dry, the women and girls tie them together in tall stacks and carry them to the markets.

Tanzania was the first Bantu country in Africa to win its freedom from colonial rule. The new government built huge silos for grain on the central plains as a protection against famine in times of drought. There, the Gogo people are encouraged to store their grain. As they empty their sacks of grain into the silos during harvest time, they make the work easier with melodious rhythmic chanting, for the Gogo Bantu love to sing.

Boys and girls sing in unison as they crowd about the village storyteller after sundown. The golden glow that comes with dusk and the cool of night that follows quickly, bring relief from the hot winds that blow across the plains.

The Gogo tribes' constant dread of hunger and famine is reflected in their great interest in stories of droughts and hard times.

The Story

The animals were in a terrible way; drought had struck the land. The water holes dried up. The lakes shrank until only oozy muddy water remained. The rivers moved sluggishly. The plains were dry and brown. No crops grew so that the thirsty animals were hungry too. The months went by, but still no rain fell.

At last, only Chameleon, Chicken, and Lion were left. Chameleon was so weak from hunger that he clung to a tree trunk. He even turned the same dirty brown color as the tree.

Chicken had a little energy left. She scratched in the dirt and found a patch of grain hidden under a stone near Chameleon's tree. She pecked at the grain until not one piece was left. And with each mouthful she ate, Chicken's strength returned. My, but she felt good!

Lion watched Chicken getting fatter by the minute. And Chameleon's eyes, swiveling every which way with anxiety, were fixed on Lion. He saw Lion creep very slowly toward Chicken.

"You are nice and fat, Chicken," Lion panted weakly. "I'm going to eat you up."

Then Lion heard a harsh voice call from the tree trunk. "No you don't! If you eat Chicken, I will eat you."

"Who said that?" Lion jerked his head up, stared at the tree trunk, but saw nothing and heard nothing. He shrugged and turned again toward Chicken. "You are nice and fat, Chicken. I'm going to eat you up."

The voice came from the tree trunk again. "No you don't! If you eat Chicken, I will eat you."

Lion was puzzled—afraid too—but hunger made him desperate. "I don't care," he said. "Chicken, I'm going to eat you up—right now." He started to pounce on poor Chicken.

Something spat on Lion and the voice growled, "Now I'm going to eat you up—fast."

Lion was terrified. He lowered his tail and slunk into the bushes.

Chicken stared and stared at the tree trunk, but saw nothing. "I can't see you, but you saved my life. Who are you?" she clucked.

"I'm Chameleon." He changed his color back to red and gold right there. "See?"

"Thank you, friend Chameleon, thank you. I would like to reward you for your kindness."

Chicken laid an egg, which Chameleon gobbled up quickly, shell and all.

"Thank you, friend Chicken, thank you. You have saved my life too." Chameleon said, changing to a bright orange color in gratitude.

Most of the time when you help other people they will help you.

6. The Rain Makers

A STORY FROM THE CHAGGA PEOPLE

The People

In northern Tanzania among the foothills and on the slopes of Africa's highest mountain, Kilimanjaro, the Chagga tribes make their home. Unlike most other Bantu tribespeople who live in village kinship groups, each Chagga family has its own farm with separate cattle kraals and storage barns. And though they follow the general pattern and build round houses, they make them taller and wider, with thick thatching that extends from the ground to the tips of the roofs. Sometimes little spires and steel rods, set in the thatching, act as lightning conductors.

Because of the climate an abundance of products can be grown—corn and sorghum, onions and cotton, bananas in the foothills, and coffee on the mountain slopes. Chagga farmers thrive and many are very prosperous.

Almost as many Chagga people live in towns as on

farms. In Moshi—an important city for the marketing of coffee—stately Chagga women move through the streets wearing colorful cotton gowns, adorned with necklaces and many bracelets. They may be on their way to shop in the open market, or to the community center to choose books from the lending library.

Except for very young children and babies, who wear strings of white beads to bring them luck, few children are seen on the streets during school hours. Chagga people know how valuable an education is and parents make sure that their children attend classes regularly.

The young people also find plenty of time for games. School teams compete in football matches. Boys, wearing white linen shirts and shorts, play cricket. Girls in skirts or tunics play volleyball. But whether the boys and girls are sophisticated town dwellers or country farmers, they still delight in the hour that is given to storytelling.

Although the rainfall is higher in northern Tanzania than on the central plains, the Chagga people have a long dry season that starts in June and ends in November. So they too tell stories that are concerned with droughts.

The Story

When the animals came to the lake one sundown they found that it had dried up. "The Rain Spirit is angry with us," they wailed. "He has taken away the water that gives us life. We suffer from hunger, we die of thirst. What can we do to appease him?"

The animals decided to combine their pleas to the great

spirit. Elephant raised his trunk and trumpeted loudly. Leopard grunted until his throat ached. Lion roared, Hyena howled, Jackal whined, Buffalo bellowed, Donkey brayed. Even Bird added his shrill cackles, peeps, and screeches to the appeals to the Rain Spirit. Giraffe, who makes very little sound considering his tremendous size, stretched his neck way up to the sky instead. The animals watched and waited anxiously for a response to their pleas. But the Rain Spirit failed them. It did not rain.

Frog crawled out from under some dried reeds. "I know how to plead to the Rain Spirit," he boasted. "Go and dig deep holes in readiness."

Usually, the animals and birds had little respect for Frog's judgment, but in desperation they followed the suggestion. They dug deep holes and waited.

Frog called to his friends. Together they sounded a chorus of croaks so loud that the thorn trees swayed under the blast and the savanna grasses wilted. Their croaks shook the earth; they pierced the sky. The Rain Spirit heard. He sent rain. The holes filled with water and the animals drank. Satisfied, they scattered over the plain or into the jungles or up on the mountaintops. But Frog preferred to make his home in the slushy mushy mud.

The wild creatures always listen for Frog's croaking during times of drought, for when they hear the earth-shaking croaks they rejoice and say, "Good! The Rain Spirit will hear our friend and he will send life-giving rain."

Because he made his boast come true, Frog won the trust of wild animals that has lasted up to the present.

7. How Frog Lost His Tail

A STORY FROM THE SUKUMA PEOPLE

The People

It is not surprising that the people of East and Central Africa have woven so many stories around animals. Their land teems with wildlife. Between the homes of the Chagga Bantu and the Sukuma Bantu, Tanzania's largest tribal group, spread the Serengeti plains where large animals roam freely. Browsers like elephants and giraffes reach for the leaves on treetops. Dainty antelope and striped zebra nibble the grasses, while the green eyes of the crafty leopard survey the scene from overhanging branches. The lions are the dominant animals as they stalk majestically across the savanna in search of prey.

The territory of the Sukuma tribes extends into wild-game country and around the southern shores of Lake Victoria. Sukumaland is made up of separate kingdoms, each under a chief—an *ntemi*—who on special occasions

60

wears a magnificent feathered headdress trimmed with rare shells and bits of carved ivory. Sukuma boys and girls learn the customs and traditions of their various tribes, and Sukuma history which is one of conquest and leadership. Thus, they are a proud people who resemble the Chagga in the respect they hold for education.

Today, Sukuma boys wear khaki shirts and shorts when they sail with their fathers on fishing expeditions close to the green shores and around the islands of Lake Victoria. Their single-sail boats glide over the water, while the fishermen drop great looped nets made from reeds. Thousands of hungry birds wait for a share of the catch as the men and boys haul in the nets. Sukuma people watch from the shore for a boat's return, for fish are necessary items in the Sukuma diet and the people depend on the fishermen to bring them a good catch every day.

Sometimes the men and boys fish from dugout or woven-reed canoes in the lake's long calm inlets. Then they must watch for hippopotamuses that can overturn a canoe if they suddenly pop to the surface, and for crocodiles that lurk in the shallow water among a profusion of plants and overhanging vines.

Girls wear gay, splashy patterned wrap-arounds set off with matching shawls for head coverings. From an early age they learn from their mothers how to be clever traders in the big, open markets. Included in the articles for sale are basketware and beadwork, used hats and sunglasses, combs made from stiff reeds bound with copper wire, large, round wooden spoons, and small mirrors that the girls use when styling their hair in tiny tight braids.

61

The market places are also centers for town gossip and for storytelling. Many of the animal stories one hears near Lake Victoria are told in other towns and villages in East and Central Africa.

The Story

Frog squatted in his muddy home on the edge of the water hole. He felt miserable. He knew he was ugly, with a mouth like a black cave and protruding eyes like door-knobs. And his figure! Frog worried because he thought he resembled nothing better than an old potato that has gone to seed. Frog's chief grievance was that he had no tail.

Each day at sundown when the forest and savanna animals came to drink, they swished their tails and jeered at Frog because he was ugly. So Frog went to the Sky God. He implored the great spirit to improve his appearance. "At least, give me a tail," Frog begged.

"Very well," the Sky God declared. "I will give you a tail if you will be watchman for my special well that never dries up."

Frog replied, "I will guard the well closely. Now, please, give me a tail."

Frog showed off his long, tapering tail by hopping to and fro before his new home beside the special well. Unfortunately, having such a magnificent tail as well as his responsible position made Frog conceited—and very bossy. And he never forgot or ever forgave the animals for their previous unfriendliness. Frog's arrogance became unbearable when every other water hole and well but his special charge dried up.

"Who comes to this muddy well?" Frog demanded when the animals crawled weakly in search of water to quench their thirst. Then he would shout rudely, "Go away! Go away! There is no water here. The well is dry."

The Sky God heard of Frog's behavior. He came quietly to the well and he received the same unkind treatment. The Sky God shook with anger. He punished Frog. He took away his tail and he drove him from the well.

The Sky God keeps reminding Frog of the misery he caused. Every springtime when Frog is born as a tadpole, he has a long, beautiful tail. But as he grows, his tail shrinks. It shrinks and shrinks and then it disappears.

The Sky God takes the tail away because Frog was once spiteful and unforgiving.

8. How Chameleon Became King of the Animals

A STORY FROM THE BAGANDA PEOPLE

The People

Frog has another problem if he lives beside Lake Victoria. Water birds, such as pelicans and herons, watch for the chance to swoop on Frog and snatch him for their suppers. If any one of the greedy birds flew north toward the watery horizon of the lake (which is more like a sea than a lake) he would come to Kampala, the biggest city in Uganda and the center for the Baganda Bantu tribes.

More than one million Baganda people live along the lake's west shore and far inland in gradually rising lush country. Uganda ends in the thick, steamy jungles of the so-called Mountains of the Moon. Until recently, the outside world knew so little about the Baganda country that it might have been as remote as the moon. But although Uganda was isolated, it was a powerful kingdom for many

centuries, ruled by a *kabaka,* or king. The people built
beautiful buildings of tightly woven cane with cone-
shaped roofs that reached fifty feet in height. Baganda
musicians designed harps and trumpets and drums in
unique shapes that produced an equally unique music.
Fishermen sailed in dugout canoes that were seventy feet
long. Men and boys wore long cotton robes; women and
girls wore hammered-bark skirts of fine quality.

The Baganda live pretty much as they did one hundred
years ago, except that a president has replaced the royal
line of kings and Kampala is a modern city with a University College—Makerere—that draws students from all
over Africa.

Some Baganda folktales are of kings and mighty battles
and conquests. But the best stories, and the favorites, are
about Africa's animals. They are as original as the Baganda music that draws children from their play and old
men from their seats in the sun.

The Story

Chameleon was a small helpless creature in the early days. He crawled along slowly on weak little legs in a coat that was an ugly gray color. No one paid much attention to Chameleon, for even his conversation was dull. But Chameleon learned to use his wits. He became sly and cunning.

One hot afternoon all the big animals were lounging under the trees. They did not see Chameleon who was

67

hidden behind Cheetah whom he envied for his speed and strength.

Presently Cheetah lifted his head. "Look who's coming across the savanna," he said. "It's old King Lion himself."

The animals watched King Lion strolling toward them. Lion flopped on the ground and rested his head on his paws. He looked bored.

"It's no fun sitting on that throne alone all day," Lion yawned. "Anyone who wants the job of being king can have it."

Silence. Each animal longed to be king, but not wanting to appear pushy; each was afraid to speak.

King Lion swept the flies from his ears. He pulled himself slowly to his feet and stretched. "We'll have a race," he announced. "Whoever gets to the throne first wins."

King Lion chose the starting point for each animal. "You, Slowpoke Tortoise, start way up front. You, Elephant, start here. Zebra, Giraffe, Wildebeest, go back there. And Cheetah, if you don't mind, you start way, way back there."

Monkey, Baboon, Warthog, Eland—all the animals were given a starting point. No one noticed sly Chameleon.

"Everybody ready?" King Lion roared. "GO!"

Tortoise toddled, Hippopotamus waddled, Elephant ambled, Zebra and Wildebeest galloped, Monkey skipped, and Giraffe paced. But Cheetah outran them all. He reached the throne a full ten minutes before the other animals came into sight.

Cheetah started to sit on the throne, but a voice startled him and something held on to his tail.

"Look out!" Chameleon squealed, letting go of Cheetah's tail and settling down on the throne's crimson velvet cushion. "Don't sit on me."

"What's this?" Cheetah gasped, looking around. "You got here first?"

"Certainly! Everyone thinks you are the fastest animal in the world but, my dear Cheetah, I won the race."

As each animal panted to a stop he joined the circle around Chameleon. When Slowpoke Tortoise at last arrived a chorus of cheers proclaimed Chameleon as their new king.

Chameleon felt so happy and important that he learned a new trick right then. He changed his color through orange, yellow, and green to crimson to match the velvet that draped his beautiful gold throne.

But trickery seldom triumphs. Chameleon had plenty of time to regret the cunning scheme that had made him King of the Animals, for he had few friends as he sat in lonely majesty on his handsome throne.

9. The Tug of War

A STORY FROM THE BALUBA PEOPLE

The People

Climbing over the Mountains of the Moon and traveling west into the Congo, one passes through rain forests that seem to stretch on forever. Paths through the forest are carpeted with layers of fallen leaves. One feels inclined to tread carefully, for the forest floor is always moist. Gentle earth odors rise, a breeze murmurs through the foliage, the grasses quiver. A pale sun is barely visible through mists and treetops. There are noises of living things—of birds singing in the trees, of vultures wheeling high in the air, and of insects tunneling in the tree trunks. Rising smoke, the sound of shouting and singing, and the hollow rumble of tom-toms indicate the nearness of a village, perhaps concealed behind a banana grove.

The majority of the Congolese people still live in bush country. They get around either on foot or in dugout canoes. But the Congo's modern cities throb with the busy comings and goings of town dwellers who are thoroughly at home in planes and cars. Beyond the screen of low trees to the south of the rain forest, lie the Congo's broad savannas. Here are the homes of the Baluba Bantu tribes, many of whom work in the Katanga copper mines. Most Baluba people speak as fluently in French as in their own language, for their country until recently was under Belgian rule.

Traditional songs and dances bring great pleasure to the Baluba, and they carefully preserve them for festive occasions. Out come the drums followed by dance leaders wearing fantastic wooden masks trimmed with streaming raffia-palm fiber and shells. Out come the girl dancers, bedecked in gorgeous beads and plumes. They bend to the earth and touch it with their hands. Suddenly, the girls fling back their hands and flap them in the air, up and down, up and down, like birds. Boy dancers spin about, make broad perilous leaps while timing their movements to the thumping of the drums. A ripple of joy spreads through the audience and eyes gleam like brush fires.

Excited listeners press close against the storyteller when they see him poking at the fire. Laughter is near the surface, for Baluba stories are usually filled with whimsy and good humor.

The Story

Porcupine's ambition was to be called "Friend" by Elephant and Hippopotamus, the biggest and strongest

animals in the jungle. But Elephant and Hippopotamus would have nothing to do with Porcupine.

Every waking hour Porcupine tried to think of ways to win their respect. One day he saw Elephant going into the jungle. He followed quietly. When he came to the place where Elephant was taking a nap on a mossy patch he said, "Good morning, Friend."

Elephant rose up in anger. He raised his trunk and rumbled, "Don't call *me* Friend, Small-creature-of-no-importance."

"Just a minute, Elephant," Porcupine interrupted. "I may be small but I am stronger than you are. Let us have a tug-of-war and I will prove it."

Porcupine unrolled a long rope. He gave one end to Elephant. "This is your end, Elephant. I will take the

other end and then we'll tug. We won't stop until one of us wins or the rope breaks."

Porcupine ran into the jungle with his end of the rope. He ran to where Hippopotamus splashed and blew bubbles in the river.

"Hey, Friend," Porcupine shouted. "Come ashore."

Hippopotamus climbed out of the river in a hurry. He bellowed, "Don't call *me* Friend, Small-creature-of-no-importance."

"Just a minute, Hippopotamus. I may be small but I am stronger than you are. Let us have a tug-of-war and I will prove it." Porcupine showed Hippopotamus the rope.

"This is your end," Porcupine said. "We won't stop until one of us wins or the rope breaks."

Porcupine dashed back to the jungle. When he came to the middle of the rope he picked it up and shook it. Immediately the tugging began. The rope tightened. It quivered. It was pulled first one way. Then it was pulled the other.

Porcupine rested against a log and watched the rope strain and quiver as first Elephant, then Hippopotamus, gave it a mighty tug. He ate a huge lunch of mushrooms and wild figs, then he took a nap.

Late in the afternoon Porcupine decided it was time to stop the tug of war. He cut the rope with one of his quills and it sprang apart.

Porcupine rushed to where Elephant lay sprawled on the ground. Elephant was holding one leg which had been sprained when he had suddenly sat down on it. His trunk was a mass of bruises from the rope.

"Friend Porcupine," said Elephant, rubbing his leg and his trunk at the same time. "I see you haven't a quill out of place. You are, indeed, equal to me in strength if not in size. We shall be Friends."

Porcupine rushed to find Hippopotamus breathing heavily and rubbing his head. "Why, Friend Porcupine," he said in a surprised voice, "you look as cool as a cucumber. You have proved that size is not everything. Let us be Friends."

After that, Porcupine and Elephant and Hippopotamus were seen together constantly. They addressed one another as "Friend" and this, as you can imagine, made Porcupine very happy indeed.

10. The Pattern on Tortoise's Back

A STORY FROM THE BEMBA PEOPLE

The People

Rolling grasslands sweep through Central Africa in an unending expanse of tall grass and scattered straggly trees. Breaks in the monotonous land show small sharp hills called kopjes that are formed by oddly shaped boulders balanced one atop the other. Rats and rabbits and varieties of wildcats find refuge in the kopjes from the bigger meat-eating animals, and from birds of prey that wait to pounce, their movements faster than a falling star.

Contained within the grasslands of Zambia, which lie just south of the Congo, are several Bantu tribal groups. Prominent among them are the Bemba tribespeople who trace their paramount chief's lineage back through fourteen generations to Mwata Yanwa, the founder of the Bemba nation. Bemba elders pay close attention to passing on tribal history to young people, and in seeing that they practice old customs and traditions. To them it is important to remember that the first Bemba tribes chose the crocodile as their emblem, or totem, when as migrating people looking for a place to settle, they came to the Kalunga River and found on the riverbank a dead crocodile. They thought that this was a good omen so they chose to build their home right there. Though Bemba elders preserve the past, they also encourage their people to go to school and especially to learn about good government. Many leaders of the new nation of Zambia have come from the Bemba Bantu tribes.

Like Katanga in the Congo, Zambia has many copper mines. Thousands of Bemba families live in towns near the mines. The children in such families have been born, have grown up, and have gone to school in towns. They wear Western-style clothing. Like young people in cities and towns all over the world, they know little of life as it exists in the back country.

But many Bemba families still live among the kopjes in the hot valleys—the grazing and hunting grounds for wild animals—or beside the lakes and swamplands which are the headwaters for Zambia's rivers. Some of the Bemba, the swamp dwellers, as they are called, still carry on the ancient custom of "silent trading" that elsewhere has been abandoned.

Silent trading is conducted at night under the fiery span of the Milky Way, or in moonlight. It is usually an exchange of grain for fish. Silent trading is a business that men and boys share.

78

Partners to the "silent trade" never see each other. Farmers drift through the dusky light in silence, bundles on their heads, ears alert for the tread of a stalking nocturnal animal. They unload their burdens at a prearranged trading post and examine the dried fish that have been left by the swamp dwellers for exchange. They consider its value, lay what they think to be a fair amount of grain beside it, then withdraw into the shadows to wait. Then the swamp dwellers come out from their hiding places. They look over the quality and quantity of grain. If they are satisfied they take it home. But should they decide that the exchange is unfair they again hide. When the farmers find their offer unacceptable, they either increase the amount of grain or pick up their baskets and glide away.

Although the swamp dwellers and the farmers rarely meet or mingle with other tribal groups, their storytellers repeat the same folktales when night falls and darkness frames the glow of Zambian village fires.

The Story

Vulture's greatest friends were Mr. and Mrs. Tortoise. He stopped in to see them at least once a week, and he stayed for a cup of tea.

One day, after Mr. Vulture had gone home, Tortoise said to his wife, "Our kind friend, Vulture, visits us every week yet we never return his call."

"Well, what can we do about it?" snapped Mrs. Tortoise. "He lives on top of the highest kopje. We can't climb that high."

"Just the same, we are impolite," her husband replied. "It is a dilemma."

"Grow longer legs and leave your shell at home. Then you can visit Vulture," suggested Mrs. Tortoise.

"You know I can't do that. But give me time. I'll think of a way out of the dilemma." Mr. Tortoise went away and thought deeply.

After a good long think Mr. Tortoise said to his wife, "I know what we can do. Tie me in a bundle and on Vulture's next visit tell him the bundle contains tobacco. Then ask him to take the bundle and trade it for grain."

"If that will make you happy I will do it," sighed Mrs. Tortoise.

Mrs. Tortoise wrapped banana leaves around her husband. She added a few tobacco leaves to make the bundle smell right. Then she tied string around the bundle and stood it in a corner.

"Where is your husband, Mrs. Tortoise?" asked Vulture when he dropped in for a visit the following day.

"He has gone to find grain, for there is none—absolutely none—in this village. Is there grain where you live?" Mrs. Tortoise asked, refilling Vulture's teacup and adding sugar.

"Yes, indeed, Mrs. Tortoise, we have plenty of grain."

Mrs. Tortoise showed him the bundle. "My husband left this sack of tobacco hoping you would be kind enough to trade it for grain."

"Certainly, certainly," Vulture said, pleased to be of service to his great friends.

He took the bundle in his strong talons and flew off with it—high up in the kopje.

Vulture was about to land on the rock beside his house when a voice called from the bundle. "This is Tortoise, your friend. I said I would pay you a visit one day and here I am."

But Mr. Vulture, astonished and surprised at hearing a voice, dropped the bundle. It bounced on the rock and poor Mr. Tortoise's shell cracked. The cracks made a crisscross pattern that have remained to this day.

If Mr. Tortoise had been less impatient the accident would never have happened.

11. How Animals Got Their Beautiful Coats

A STORY FROM THE ZULU PEOPLE

The People

Centuries ago the Bantu tribes roamed all over southern Africa looking for places to build permanent homes. When the advance tribe in the Great March came at last to the Drakensberg Mountains in South Africa, their leader was then an old, old man. He was too old and too feeble to continue, so he ordered the tribeswomen to make a large round basket with a lid. When the basket of tightly woven reeds was ready the leader told his son to take his wife and his wife's family and to step inside. They obeyed him and squeezed into the basket. The old man fastened the lid, then he pushed the basket down the mountainside. It rolled over hills and across valleys for many miles until it came to rest beside a beautiful

84

winding river. Out stepped the old man's son, his wife, and his wife's family.

Soon afterwards the wife gave birth to a son. The baby's parents named him Zulu, which means "Heaven," for they truly believed that the place where they had chosen to settle was a heaven on earth. When the baby was grown, he became the first of a long line of Zulu kings. This legend, as told by their descendants, was the story of the beginning of the Zulu warrior nation.

Zululand rises steeply from the Indian Ocean in a series of grassy slopes covered with fragrant flowering bushes and aloes. It is surrounded by cool, quiet forests where deciduous and evergreen trees grow. Many Zulu homes are situated in The Valley of a Thousand Hills, the center of Zululand.

A Zulu family's home is a dome. It resembles a large round bowl turned upside down. The people bend saplings to form the dome, then cover the saplings with straw bound firmly by long strands of finely braided grass. Zulus arrange their huts in a circle to protect the cattle kraal which they place in the center of the village. Zulus have a tremendous regard for their cattle, and Zulu kings of former days paraded their herds before visitors. It is on record that the herds of one king, Dingane, took five hours to move past a reviewing stand. Zulu boys follow the rule of caring for the cattle and girls assist their mothers in planting the fields and caring for the home.

Villagers welcome visitors with the greeting "Sakubona!" which means "We see you!" Perhaps the women

and girls are threading beads into artistic patterns for belts and bracelets, or elaborate headpieces and necklaces. Zulus weave messages called "love letters" into their necklaces. The colors they use and the relative position of one color to another are important. Usually girls weave these messages into two-inch squares and then string them together. Every color from the palest to the deepest shade, has a special subtle meaning.

The scanty clothing Zulu children wear is weighted down with beadwork. And though a girl child's hair is cut short, it is worn longer when she reaches an age to be engaged. The girl then wears a very short bead-trimmed skirt of soft calfskin. After she marries she lengthens it, and dresses her hair in elaborate styles with beads and feathers, using clay to hold it in place.

A young man wears animal skins around his waist and feathers in his hair when he calls on the parents of the girl he wants to marry. The visit is part of an old honored custom called *lobola*. The young man and the parents of the girl discuss the number of cattle he must give them as tokens of his serious intentions. For this important occasion, the young man also carries a small oxhide shield, the symbol of the warrior Zulu.

Old customs are gradually giving way in Zululand. Many young people now work in cities. Unchanging, however, is the pleasure and delight Zulus derive from storytelling. Sometimes the stories reflect the Zulus' great interest in a well-groomed appearance.

The Story

In the beginning all African animals were the same color—a dull, nondescript brown. Zebra, Giraffe, Leopard, Mongoose, Hyena, Tortoise were all the same dull brown. Hyena, in addition to being of a drab monotonous color, had a mean disposition. He liked to play tricks. Usually, he chose a smaller animal as the target for his jokes.

One day Hyena saw Tortoise shuffling through the withered bits of litter that lay on the forest path. He seized poor Tortoise, knotted a piece of vine around one of his feet, and hung him from a high branch. Tortoise dangled dangerously, but Hyena ran away laughing. Tortoise was desperate. He felt the knot slipping. At any moment he expected to crash to the ground and be killed.

Leopard came along the path, saw Tortoise, and stopped.

"Oh, Mr. Leopard, please help me," Tortoise pleaded.

Instead of making a meal of Tortoise, Leopard helped him down. He rescued him and saved his life.

Tortoise thanked Leopard. "I would like to make you beautiful because you have saved my life," he said.

Tortoise mixed a silver-yellow color from flower petals and painted Leopard's coat all over. He made little rosette patterns from the top of Leopard's head to the tip of his long thin tail.

Leopard went on his way. He met Zebra.

"My, my," Zebra exclaimed. "Where did you get that handsome coat?"

"It was given to me by my friend, Mr. Tortoise," Leopard explained.

88

Zebra went to Tortoise. "Oh, Mr. Tortoise, you gave Mr. Leopard a handsome coat. Please do the same for me."

Tortoise painted black and white stripes all over Zebra's coat. He finished the job by painting Zebra's dainty hoofs a glossy black.

Zebra, pleased and proud, went on his way. He met Giraffe.

"Oh, oh! Where did you get such a magnificent coat?" Giraffe asked.

"It was given to me by my friend, Mr. Tortoise," Zebra explained.

Giraffe went to Tortoise. "Oh, Mr. Tortoise, you gave Mr. Zebra such a magnificent coat. Please do the same for me."

Tortoise chose a cream color and a rich reddish brown for Giraffe's new coat of odd-shaped squares that looked rather like pieces in a jigsaw puzzle.

Giraffe went on his way. He met Hyena.

"Where did you get the coat?" leered Hyena in a very sneery manner.

"It was given to me by my friend, Mr. Tortoise," Giraffe explained.

Hyena went to Tortoise. "Give me a beautiful coat too," he demanded in a threatening voice. "If you don't, I'll hang you from the tree again."

Tortoise never answered. He picked up his knife slowly. Holding Hyena steady with one hand, he hacked his hair into different lengths with the other. Some hair stood on end, some lay flat, some went the wrong way. Tortoise mixed the colors together in one pot and smeared Hyena's coat all over. Hyena was blotched white, gray, and smeary brown. It was just as well he could not see himself!

Hyena has been that way ever since—the untidiest looking animal in Africa—labeled clearly as a mean and unpleasant character.

12. The Injured Lion

A STORY FROM THE SWAZI PEOPLE

The People

The Zulus won fame as a nation of warriors because they were brave fighters, but as the power of their kings increased so did their cruelty, not only toward alien tribes whom they conquered, but also toward their own people. One Zulu king's tyranny and unjust punishments forced several leading warriors to sever their tribal loyalties. Early in the nineteenth century they left Zululand with thousands of followers and started nations of their own. One group under King Sobhuza I marched north and founded Swaziland, a small idyllic country set in the middle of high mountains dotted with dense forests.

Today, King Sobhuza II reigns in Swaziland. Nowhere in Africa does a wiser king rule, or one who loves his subjects more. The Swazi people return his affection. They honor and revere their king as a true friend, and as a man of peace.

By observing every Swazi tradition with appropriate festivals, King Sobhuza II brings happiness and gaiety to his little kingdom. Bedecked in a handsome plumed headdress, and wearing a soft flowing leopard kilt and a lion mane draped around his shoulders, the king leads the planting and harvesting dances with great pomp and dignity. The dancers who follow him in time to flute notes, shake hand rattles, while their ankle rattles respond to the stamping of their feet. King Sobhuza II is a famous rain maker. During periods of drought and after a long, serious ceremony which includes appeals to the Swazi Rain Spirit, he sprinkles a special "medicine" on the newly seeded fields.

The Swazi tribes followed the Zulu custom of building homes like domes, but they adopted a quite different style of dress. Girls and women wear large cotton shawls knotted on one shoulder like Roman togas. They favor brilliantly colored print designs, usually of flowers or fish, though sometimes a bicycle or a bus is printed just where a girl sits down. As a rule girls keep their hair cut short, but when they decide to let it grow long they bleach it with lime. Married Swazi women tease their hair, padding it with bits of black wool until their coiffures reach the size of large footballs. Then they decorate the finished hairdo with beads, and wear beaded bands across the hairline on their foreheads.

Boys and men pay even more attention to dressing stylishly than do their women. They keep their hair long and bleached, and wear a feather stuck jauntily over each ear, pointing forward. If they are of royal blood, the

feathers are red. The men wear little fur pelts over striped skirts, and strings of beads across their chests.

When he chooses to wear bracelets on his upper arm, a man slips a chiffon kerchief between them letting it wave like a banner as he strides through the woods. He sings as he proceeds, and swings his knobkerrie—a wooden club with a large knobbed head. It must have been such a person who figured in one of Swaziland's favorite stories.

The Story

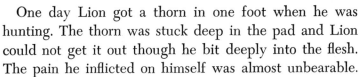

One day Lion got a thorn in one foot when he was hunting. The thorn was stuck deep in the pad and Lion could not get it out though he bit deeply into the flesh. The pain he inflicted on himself was almost unbearable.

Unless he removed the thorn his hunting days were over, for a hunter with an infected paw is finished; he is of no further use to the pride—and this Lion knew.

In desperation, Lion lay down on a path in the woods where people passed. Presently a man came marching along the path. He was frightened when he saw Lion. He dashed into the woods and hid behind a tree from which he could see Lion's movements. He saw the poor beast get up and limp painfully along the path. Then he saw him lie down again and pretend to sleep. The man understood Lion's silent appeal for help, so he advanced cautiously and inspected the terrible wound. Then drawing his knife from its sheath, he cut out the thorn. Lion jumped up quickly. The man crouched low in fear, but Lion merely ran off into the woods.

The man continued along the path until, rounding a bend and passing through a thicket, he came upon a buck, freshly killed, lying before him. He saw at once that this was Lion's token of appreciation. He skinned the buck, cut up the animal, and hung the meat from a tree. Then he hurried to his village to find help in carrying it home.

Later, the man no doubt reminded his neighbors, as they shared the feast of venison, that a kind deed brings its reward.

13. In Unity Is Strength

A STORY FROM THE BAVENDA PEOPLE

The People

The word "Bavenda" means "the people of the world," yet the Bavenda tribal group in South Africa prefer to live secluded lives far removed from outside influences. They have changed the least of any Bantu group since Europeans entered Africa. The mud huts in the Bavenda villages decorated in abstract designs lie near the Rhodesian border and the main road from South Africa. The lives of the people who live in them follow the pattern their forefathers brought from the north 200 years ago.

The Bavenda follow ancient customs in training their young people. In remote mountain forests boys and girls from about the age of eight years old undergo rigid secret discipline in separate schools. Tribal elders supervise the schools. They put students through harsh physical tests to toughen them. Sometimes they force students

to sleep in the open for long periods without clothing, and to kneel in icy mountain water for hours at a time. Boys learn old methods of hunting and fighting in their isolated schools. Girls learn obedience and the duties of motherhood. Should the boys or girls falter during their grueling ordeals, they are beaten with sticks. Occasionally there are fatalities in Bavenda schools, but young people accept the hardships and punishment because they know that when the course ends they will be full, honored tribal members.

Boys and girls finish their education when they are in their teens and after they have learned to live together in combined schools called *dombas*. Tribal dances and songs are included in their schooling, for dancing and singing are as great a part of Bavenda life as eating and sleeping.

Students learn to play musical instruments that were invented by their ancestors and which have since been adapted by musicians of other countries—the marimba and the xylophone, for example. They produce clear melodies on single-note reed flutes, and deep thundering booms on *ngoma* drums.

Students learn a spectacular dance called the Python Dance in domba schools. They form a line, one behind the other, and close enough for each dancer to grasp tightly the left elbow of the preceding dancer. A python's head is painted on the left hand of the leader in the line, and the reptile's body is painted on the forearms of the following performers. The dancers raise and drop their forearms slowly, in imitation of the undulating motion of a python. The line of dancers shuffles and sways forward,

up and down, winding through the woods, and producing the eerie realistic effect of a writhing reptile. The python is sacred to the Bavenda people, to whom it is the symbol of fertility and unity.

The Bavenda value tribal unity above everything else. Many old stories that were brought from the north and which are now repeated by other tribes in other parts of Bantu Africa stress its importance.

The Story

Three beautiful Waterbuck were great friends. They lived together in the woods, eating together, sleeping together, working together.

Unknown to the Waterbuck, Lion watched them constantly. What a nice tasty meal Waterbuck would make, were his greedy thoughts. But three Waterbuck together were more than he could tackle.

One day the three friends quarreled. They separated. Each went his own way. And Lion chuckled to himself. He followed first one Waterbuck which he killed, then a second, then a third.

There is strength in unity.

14. The Battle of the Animals

A STORY FROM THE BUSHMAN PEOPLE

The People

Before the Bantu settled in Central and southern Africa tribes of shorter stature, speaking languages filled with clicks and pops, lived there as nomads. They were the Bushmen and the Hottentots whose origins nobody knows exactly. The coming of the Bantu migrants was disastrous for these people whose height averaged five feet, one inch. The newcomers were bigger, stronger, more aggressive, and better equipped, with long-bladed spears for attack and stout oxhide shields for defense. The arrows of the Bushmen and the Hottentots were no match for the Bantus' superior weapons. The few little people who were not killed by the invaders gradually retreated farther south.

Where could they find land that was safe from the spears of the Bantu and would be exclusively theirs? How

101

could they escape being forced to work for white men whom they found already living in South Africa? Some Hottentots were absorbed by marriage into the Bantu and white races; others found a refuge in South West Africa. But the tenacious Bushmen pushed on. Their search ended in the Kalahari Desert, a dry desolate expanse of rolling sand dunes and thorny tussock that spread over several thousand square miles in the country of Botswana.

Humanity had avoided this desert land until the Bushmen adapted themselves to living in its environment of no lakes, no rivers, and no rainfall for nine months. And there were no shadows except those thrown by the spindly thorn trees and the bottle-shaped baobab trees.

Of slight build, though wiry, the Bushmen contrast with other racial groups in Africa, being of a light tan color, and having high foreheads, small noses, and the wide-set eyes of Orientals. Men and women wear leather loinclothes that hang longer in the back to give them something to sit on. Women wear a leather sling over their shoulders in which they carry their babies.

The Bushmen have no chiefs or headmen, but live as a family—a man and his wives and other female dependents. Each member of a Bushman family has a specific duty. Women and girls dig for root vegetables with sharpened sticks. The younger children search in the long dry grass for tsama melons and long eland cucumbers which supply them with moisture. It seems that Bushmen are constantly searching for food. But this activity is a necessity in order for them to survive.

Bushman hunters roam over the desert, their sharp eyes alert for deadly snakes and scorpions while they look for one of the varieties of antelope that frequent the desert. They are excellent marksmen and rarely miss a target with their short arrows made of bone or metal and poisoned with a certain beetle pupa and powdered cobra

103

venom that has been mixed with gum. The hunters stalk the wounded animal, sometimes for a day, before the poison takes effect and the animal dies.

Every member of the group, excited and gleeful, helps in conserving the hide, the flesh, the entrails, and the bones of every catch, for Bushmen do not hunt for pleasure but for food and water. First the poisoned portion of the animal is carefully cut away and discarded. Then using great care the Bushman leader cuts through the antelope hide and removes the rumen—the "first" stomach —in which antelopes store food and water. The onlookers cluck with pleasure when they see him pour the precious liquid from it into a leather container. Then he squeezes the half-digested grass in the rumen to extract the last drop of liquid.

When they are back in their village or *werf* as the Bushmen call their cluster of temporary low grass shelters, the adult members of the family prepare a feast. What meat they do not cook and eat at once they dry against future hunger periods. For days after a successful hunt, Bushman children pick out and eat the marrow from the bones. The women make smoking pipes and utensils from the dried and hollow bones.

Ostrich eggs also provide food for the Bushmen. And the blown shells provide them with water containers. The girls and women make beads from the small pieces of broken shells by shaping the pieces of shell with their teeth. Their necklaces are often adorned with small tortoises that have been hollowed into containers for holding grease and fats as aids to beauty. The Bushman woman's jewelry also includes carved bone beads, grass beads, and colored beads fashioned from the roots of plants.

When the Bushmen lived in Central Africa they were creative graphic artists. They used brilliant earth colors to cover the walls of caves and overhanging ledges with action pictures that contained hundreds of figures of men and animals. The beautiful paintings remain as mute testimony to a more leisurely life. The Bushmen today satisfy their artistic senses with music, using stringed instruments to accompany their mellow singing voices. And they have preserved stories that are as filled with variety and action as were their paintings of former days. Bushman storytellers like to recall stories of earlier days when they and the Hottentots lived closer to earth's riches.

The Story

Terrible rivalry existed between the Winged Creatures and the Animals on Earth. They argued whenever they met by the water hole. The Winged Creatures boasted about their power of flight. The Animals on Earth boasted about their strength. They exchanged rude remarks and insults.

Vulture squawked. Hyena laughed. The Go'way Bird shrieked. Lion roared that they must have a battle—a mighty battle—to decide, once and for all, which of the two groups was the more powerful. Each side must choose an umpire, Lion suggested.

The Winged Creatures chose the Bird That Cannot

Fly as their umpire. They ordered Ostrich to hold his long neck straight up when the battle went well for the Winged Creatures.

The Animals on Earth chose Jackal as their umpire. Jackal was a coward. He was afraid to fight. Lion said that Jackal was bad for morale. He ordered Jackal to stand on a high anthill, to hold his thick tail high when the battle went well for the Animals on Earth.

When the mighty battle began, Eagle led the Winged Creatures. With Sun behind them, they swooped upon the Animals on Earth. When the big animals looked into the dazzling light they were confused.

Thousands of screeching loud-voiced Winged Creatures attacked the animals. Millions of tiny birds, moths, butterflies, locusts, and cockroaches came down as one big cloud. They surrounded the Animals on Earth, stung them, and blinded them. The Winged Creatures were winning the battle and the Animals on Earth, disunited, started to run away.

But that deceitful Jackel cheated. He continued to hold his thick tail high.

Lion saw the thick tail waving like a victory banner. He roared an order to the Animals on Earth. "Come back! Come back and unite! We are winning!"

The Animals on Earth returned. They united. They charged the Winged Creatures. They drove them off with loud stampings, slashings, trumpetings, and bellowings. At one moment it seemed to be all over for the Winged Creatures.

But little Honey Guide, an observant bird, rushed to

108

Eagle. "General Eagle, listen to me. We are losing because of Jackal," she twittered. "The coward cheated. He held his thick tail high when his side was losing."

"Humph!" Eagle drew his neck in. He crouched low, shook his feathers. "Send Bee to me," he ordered.

Bee received a special order. He buzzed off on a very special mission. Bee felt important. He was going to win the battle for the Winged Creatures. Bee felt pretty sure of that!

Bee followed a roundabout course. He buzzed around the low bushes and through the tall trees. Bee buzzed around the anthill where Jackal stood with his thick tail held high. Jackal grinned because his trick had worked. He grinned and chuckled and giggled to himself. But Jackal's chuckles were soon to end!

Bee traveled as fast as a rocket toward Jackal, and stung him on the tail! Jackal dropped his tail, yelped with pain, and dashed for cover.

The Animals on Earth saw their victory signal fall. "The battle is lost," they wailed in chorus. And they turned and fled.

That is how the Winged Creatures won the mighty battle with the Animals on Earth many years ago in Botswana.

It only proves that cowards and cheats never win!

15. The Bird With the Most Beautiful Song

A STORY FROM THE PYGMY PEOPLE

The People

Far to the north of the parched Kalahari Desert lie thousands of square miles of the earth's surface that rarely sees the sun. Perpetual twilight hangs over the Congo's Ituri forest. Towering trees—reaching sometimes to 150 feet—compete for space and light. Tangled creepers and vines press down and clog the dense damp underbrush.

Small people live in the depths of the Ituri forest. They are the nomadic Pygmy tribes who number approximately 30,000. They are known collectively as the Bambuti.

Unlike the Bushmen, whose homes are beaten by the sun, the Bambuti are apt to wilt if they leave the shadows. Pygmy heads are large; their legs are short in proportion

110

to their muscular arms and bodies. A male Pygmy's average height is four feet, eight inches; a woman's is four feet, four inches. The men of a few rare Pygmy groups average as little as four feet, three inches. Bambuti clothing is minimal. They wear bark cloth passed between their legs and looped, back and front, over a woven belt.

The Bambuti are elusive and shy of strangers, but among themselves and outsiders whom they trust they are friendly and fun-loving. They clap their hands and sing loudly when they march over obscure forest trails, warning prowling animals like leopards and buffalo to keep out of the way. Perhaps the group of families is moving to a new campsite because it holds promise of a richer supply of wild game.

Putting up the huts on a new site is a community project accompanied by plenty of laughter and singing and joke-telling as an expression of Pygmy joy in sharing the beauty and tranquility of forest living. To build their huts Pygmies drive pliable saplings into the ground to form a circle. They bend the tips and tie them at the top, making a frame which they cover with overlapped broad leaves, leaving one small, low entrance.

For food, the Bambuti forage in the forest for tidbits such as fruits, roots, frogs, leaves, caterpillars, and mushrooms. The Pygmies add them to the stewpot or roast them along with meat caught by their hunters.

The Pygmies' hunting system needs the cooperation of the members of at least six families. Each family contributes its own hunting net several feet wide and many yards long, made from the stems of a tough vine. The

men and boys stake the nets firmly, end to end, to form one great wide loop in a part of the forest where game is most likely to hide. They take up positions behind their particular length of net and with spears poised or bow and arrow ready, wait for the women and the girls to drive the game toward the open side of the circled nets. Hand clapping and shouting surprise the animals which take fright and rush, panic-stricken, into the trap. Varieties of antelope and small bush pigs are among the captives that fall to the spears of the hunters.

The Bambuti immediately stop work when a hunter returns to camp with the exciting news that he has killed an elephant. The men may be mending their nets or pounding bark into cloth. The women may be painting their bodies with vegetable dyes in special patterns or weaving belts from fibers. The boys and girls may be fishing in a nearby river or swinging on a conveniently looped vine. They stop whatever they are doing, break camp, and move en masse to a new camp near the carcass.

Even in the Ituri forest news travels quickly. Other bands of Pygmies converge. They too set up camps until every vestige of the bountiful supply of meat is eaten. Sometimes the tribes that live outside the forest venture in to share the feast, though to them the mysterious deep woods are filled with sinister evil spirits that curse the soil.

The Bambuti would have nothing to do with outsiders if they could avoid it, but a sort of trade arrangement brings them marching out of their dimly lit retreat once in a while, bearing game or ivory or skins, and everyone's favorite—wild honey. They pause long enough among their business associates to relate one or two tall tales to heighten still farther the outsider's fear of the forest spirits, then they march right back again. The bartered goods they carry home include farm products and tools, salt, tobacco, and cloth.

One occasion, the *Molimo*, a festival, gives full scope to the Pygmies' imagination and sense of fun. Bambuti men claim that the Molimo is a special forest spirit that periodically visits them. In preparation for the important occasion each Bambuti family places food in a basket that hangs from a tree. The women are banished to the huts; for Molimo is strictly taboo to women. And though they suspect that Molimo is a man-made thing, the women play the game. They are like children who have lost a belief in Santa Claus but find pleasure in pretending.

At first a distant sound reaches the camp—it comes closer—singing, sighing, high, low, loud, soft. It could be the wailing of wind in the trees, the bellowing of buffalo, the cooing of doves. The sound expresses the gamut of emotions from the moaning sorrow of the bereaved to the warmth of love and the joys and delights of forest freedom. Molimo sounds circle the camp—louder, louder—then they recede until they are faraway echoes. Young men dance and old men sing as they hunch over their fires eating the contents of the special baskets, for no man must sleep during Molimo's singing although it may last all night and every night for many weeks.

In reality, the Molimo is a musical instrument that resembles a long trumpet fashioned from portions of the

114

trunk of the molimo, a tree with a soft center which is easily scooped out. Two men carry the Molimo. The first man supports the trumpet end shoulder-high while the master musician blows his ingenious imitations through the other end. When the festival terminates the Molimo is hidden, with ceremony, high in the branches of a tall tree in a remote corner of the forest.

The Bambuti use great imagination in the stories they tell. When the camp's most gifted storyteller beckons the people to come hear his tale, he repeats adventures wherein the Bambuti outwit their powerful enemies. But the Bambuti also tell stories that convey their deep feeling and affection for the forests. They are stories that are filled with poignancy and charm.

The Story

One day a boy walked in the forest and he heard a song. It was the Most Beautiful Song in the Forest. The boy followed the sound. He peered through bushes and he saw Bird swinging on a vine. Although Bird continued singing his Most Beautiful Song, the boy saw that Bird was hungry and he put out his hand and lifted Bird and placed him gently in his small leather pouch. Then he took Bird back to camp to feed him.

The boy's father was angry. Why waste food on a strange bird, he argued. But the boy was very persuasive. His father fed Bird, the boy took him back to the forest, and Bird resumed singing his Most Beautiful Song.

The next day the boy walked in the forest and he

heard the song again. And again he saw that Bird was hungry so he took him back to camp to feed him. The boy's father was angrier than ever. Why waste food on a strange bird, he argued. But he fed Bird, the boy took him back to the forest, and Bird resumed singing his Most Beautiful Song.

The next day the boy walked in the forest and he came to where Bird sang his Most Beautiful Song. Once more he saw that Bird was hungry, so he took him back to camp to feed him.

The boy's father was so angry that he ordered the boy to leave Bird and go away.

When the boy was gone, his father killed Bird. And the Song died. The father killed the Song when he killed Bird. He robbed the forest of some of its beauty.

16. The Mighty Warrior in Hare's House

A STORY FROM THE MASAI PEOPLE

The People

The proud and haughty Masai tribesmen graze their cattle on the savannas and highlands of Kenya and Tanzania. Tradition binds them to cattle, for they believe that their God laid a carpet from Heaven to Earth over which the cattle passed as gifts for the Masais alone. In time, acquiring cattle and being fearless warriors became their two overwhelming passions. The Masais kept themselves aloof from governments and refused to obey laws imposed upon them by outsiders. The only laws they recognized were dictated by nature. When drought withered the grass they moved their herds to greener pastures, indifferent to the trampled lands they left behind them.

Non-Masai tribespeople objected to the theft of their

118

cattle. Wildlife conservationists resented the lessening in the numbers of wild creatures; many thousands of them died from thirst when Masai cattle monopolized the drinking places. The Masais needed to be educated in better herding practices.

Being highly intelligent people, the Masais have responded to reason. They are learning, gradually, to keep smaller herds. One sees fewer tall, arrogant warriors dressed traditionally, for many young Masai men now work in towns; a few are learning to be farmers.

The traditional Masai costume is picturesque. The one piece of clothing a warrior wears, except a stabbing knife thrust into a leather belt, is a short ochre-colored cape. But he paints his body with a mixture of sheep's fat and red ochre, from his nose and lips to his feet, which are shod in leather sandals. He wears many beads around his neck and his forearms and through the tops of his ears. Large copper ornaments dangle from his earlobes which are stretched until they almost touch his shoulders. With his hair tightly braided and supplemented with cattle hair and stiffened with fat, a Masai warrior makes a formidable picture as he stands on a hilltop and leans on a long-bladed spear and painted buffalo-hide shield.

The Masais use mud and clay to build low, flat huts which are little more than mounds. They keep their cattle within the *manyatta* which comprises several mounded dwellings surrounded by thornbush fences to keep out meat-eating animals.

The Masais' food is generally restricted to a mixture of

milk and blood. The blood is taken from a vein in a cow's neck that is made to swell with a tightly bound tourniquet.

A girl's upbringing follows the usual African pattern. She sees her mother molding jars and pots and she learns to imitate her. In addition she helps to mind the younger children, milk the cows, gather firewood, and haul water. As a girl grows older she designs ingenious and artistic methods of stringing varicolored beads which she wears as heavy necklaces or bracelets. Around her ankles she wears wide copper rings.

A boy's life, from his birth to his adulthood, follows definite stages. As a newborn baby he is given a calf, born at the same time, which is named for him. The boy is brother to the calf as earnestly as if it were human. Calf and boy grow together, and should the calf suffer harm at the hands of any person the boy avenges the injury.

A boy watches the cattle until his early teens, then with his contemporaries he is sent away from his village into the wild country to fend for himself. Bow and arrows are the boy's weapons, and with them he must collect a required number of birds whose feathers he must add to a trailing headdress.

The next stage in growing up takes the boy to a warrior school. There he learns the rudiments of fighting. Hour after hour for many days he practices throwing a heavy spear at a moving target which is grass bunched on a stick thrown by his instructor. He learns to be strong and brave in the novice's school, to face danger without flinching, to be honest and fair. When the boy's performance satisfies his teacher, he is ready to enter the warriors' manyatta. Then his father gives him a spear, a sword, a shield; his mother shaves his head.

A boy's last challenge is to spear and kill a lion single-handedly—a custom that is fast dying out. When he accepts the challenge and succeeds, his friends shout with joy and jump high in the air as if on springs. He is indeed a hero! And the boy wears the lion's mane as a badge of his courage and endurance.

With his growing-up ordeals behind him, a boy looks for work. Today, many young Masai people are studying in the schools and colleges of Kenya and Tanzania. They are drifting away from old customs. In towns they watch television programs, in schools they study and prepare papers.

But the boys who return to the manyatta of their forefathers follow traditions that have existed for centuries. On warm evenings in the foothills of great mountains, when the breeze has dropped and the sun is setting, they and their wives and children form a circle around the community fire. The only sounds are the calls of night birds and a distant tumbling waterfall as the storyteller commences his tale.

The Story

One day Hare who lived in a little house in a hollow tree trunk, took his basket to the field to find vegetables for his dinner. He picked wild spinach. He dug up a few yams. When Hare's basket was filled to the top he turned and went back home.

But when Hare reached his house he saw footprints on the pebbly path leading to the doorway. He heard a noise behind the front door. Someone was inside his house!

"Who is in my house?" called Hare.

A deep rumbling voice answered. "It is I—the Mighty Warrior. I can crush Rhinoceros and make mincemeat of Elephant. I am Earth's strongest creature."

"Dear, dear," said Hare to himself. "What can a small animal like myself do with such a fierce creature?" He asked Jackal, who was passing, to help him.

Jackal barked, "Who is in my friend's house?" But when Jackal heard the reply he said, "There is nothing I can do to help—nothing," and trotted off in a hurry.

Hare fetched Leopard. "Who is in my friend's house?" snarled Leopard. But when he heard the reply he loped away saying, "If he crushes Rhinoceros and makes mincemeat of Elephant he will do the same to me."

Hare asked Rhinoceros to come to his assistance.

"Who is in my friend's house?" grunted Rhinoceros. When he heard the reply he snorted, "What! He can crush me to the earth! No thanks! This is no place for me," and off he galloped.

Hare, in despair, looked for Elephant.

Elephant trumpeted, "Who is in my friend's house?" But when the fierce reply came he said, "I have no wish to be trampled underfoot and made into mincemeat," and he ambled away.

Frog heard the noise. He came hopping over to see what it was all about.

Hare ran to Frog. "Please, oh please, make the Mighty

Warrior who is earth's strongest creature leave my house," he pleaded.

Frog hopped to the door. "Who is in my friend's house?" he croaked in his deepest, most growling voice. Instead of hopping away when he heard the rumbling reply, he hopped closer.

"I, the Great Leaper, have come," Frog roared. He hopped right through the doorway and into the house.

And what did Frog see crouching in a corner?

"I am only a little caterpillar playing a joke on the big animals," said a tiny creature in a trembling voice.

The big animals came out from behind the trees. They seized poor Caterpillar and threw him high into the bushes.

Practical jokers should choose their victims wisely.

17. A Lot of Silence Makes a Great Noise

A STORY FROM THE SWAHILI PEOPLE

The People

The Swahili people are made up of many different races whose ancestors first landed, and traded, and finally settled along the fertile coastland of eastern Africa, from the Somalia border in the north to Mozambique in the south. Africa's dark interior and its inhabitants were undisturbed for many centuries. Rugged mountain ranges that in places sprawl within ten miles of the Indian Ocean and unnavigable rivers full of rapids and crocodiles acted as barriers to exploration.

But the coastal area buzzed with activity. First came the Arabs in their dhows, large single-masted boats, sometimes handsomely carved and inlaid with intricate mosaics. The Arabs built towns along the east coast and started trading with Persians, Chinese, Malayans, and with other Arabs who sailed in on the trade winds bearing cloth and jewels and foodstuffs to exchange for rhinoceros horn, elephant ivory, and slaves. Later, the Portuguese, who were famous navigators in the fifteenth century, commanded the east coast of Africa for two hundred years. Then came Indians who settled permanently and who set up businesses as shopkeepers in the towns.

The Arabs and other foreigners intermarried with the Africans and their descendants are the Swahili of today.

A new language, Ki-Swahili, emerged from the intermingling of races. Precise yet soft and pleasing to hear, Ki-Swahili, or Swahili as it is generally called, is classed with the Bantu languages. The Arabs gave it its first written form and introduced Swahili into Central Africa. Today it is the most widely spoken language in Africa south of the equator. If you were to say *Akili yapita male* (Wisdom is better than wealth) anywhere in East African countries, or in the Congo and Zambia, you would be understood.

Today's Swahili people may have a common language, but it would be easier to separate and describe the fish that swim in the ocean than to fully describe the appearance of the Swahili people, they are so various. Although East African countries such as Kenya and Tanzania are nations with Bantu leaders, many members of their governments have Arabic or Indian names. Yet in appearance these men may resemble Bantu more closely than other government members who have Bantu names. Take a stroll through a coastal city such as Dar-es-Salaam. You

will see merchants wearing the traditional full white trousers and waist-
coats of India, and other merchants
wearing long white Arab robes. But
today the majority of the people wear
Western-style clothing, though some
women and girls adapt beautiful bold-
patterned cotton prints to loose flowing robes that compete in style with
the silk saris worn by Indian women.
The cap called a fez, worn by Moslem
men, is prominent because most of the
Swahili people follow the Moslem
religion.

The Swahili live in houses that are
as diversified as the Swahili people. In
a residential area a round thatched
house may share a fence with a Euro-
pean-style bungalow surrounded by
green lawns and graced with flowering shrubs. Large houses of Arab design stand in narrow streets. In

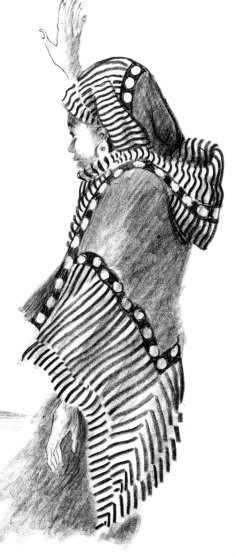

appearance they are rundown and shabby, but their magnificent carved wooden doors and latticed windows are evidences of Arab influence of former days.

During the period when Britain governed Kenya as a colony and Tanzania as a protectorate, their administrators introduced English sports. Young Swahili people meet for a set of tennis or a game of Rugby football after school. And men play golf on well-tended courses.

The coastal area of East Africa still buzzes with activity. But today the Swahili are involved with progress. They are building roads between new factories and busy ports on the Indian Ocean.

The Swahilis' greatest efforts are directed toward education. Serious students concentrate on preparations for a higher specialized education at East Africa's colleges which offer a choice of subjects that prepare students for scholarships at overseas universities. But the University College in Dar-es-Salaam has plans for the building of Tanzania's own university.

Despite East Africa's preoccupation with progress, the tales and fables that originated centuries ago are not neglected. The Swahili people are rich in folktales that have their origins in peoples from many places.

The Story

Monkey, whose name in Swahili is "Kima," lived near the seashore in East Africa. There was nothing Monkey liked more than to climb a certain tree that grew beside the ocean. The tree's great limbs swung out above the water. They were so heavy with foliage that they dipped and almost touched the waves that lapped the shore.

Every day Monkey climbed the tree and ate the fruit that grew high in its branches. He had a friend who waited in the water down below for Monkey to throw food to him. The friend was Shark, whose name in Swahili is "Papa."

One day Shark said to Monkey, "Kima, my friend, I would like to repay your kindness. Will you come with me to visit my home?"

"That is impossible, Papa," answered Monkey. "We monkeys drown if we venture too far out into the ocean."

"Don't worry about that. No water will touch you, for I will carry you on my back. Please come with me."

Monkey hesitated, but Shark was very persuasive.

"Our King is very ill," Shark said slyly when they were halfway to his home. "A monkey's heart is the only medicine that will help him."

Monkey's tiny heart went *thump-thump-thump* with fright. He held tightly to Shark's fin, kept quiet, and tried to think. How could he escape from this awful situation!

"Why don't you say something, Kima?" Shark asked, tired of the monkey's long silence.

"It is a great pity that you did not mention it sooner," Kima replied. "Then I would have brought my heart."

"What! Don't you have it with you?"

"Indeed not! We monkeys always hang our hearts on the branches when we leave the trees. I am willing to go back for it if you want to—just to be obliging."

Shark turned about with a sweep of his tail that sent

ripples outward in a wide circle. He headed for the shore.

When they came again to the tree Monkey said, "Wait for me, Papa. I will be only a minute."

Monkey scampered nimbly up the tree. He sat down, stayed quiet and after many minutes had passed, Shark called to him:"Where are you, friend Kima? It is time we were going." He listened intently for Monkey's reply, but all that he heard were leaves rustled by a breeze that wafted in from the ocean.

After many more minutes of waiting, Shark called a second time, "Where are you, friend Monkey. It is time we were going." He listened intently for Monkey's reply, but all that he heard was the musical peeping of birds preparing for sleep. Shark swam homeward under the stars.

A lot of silence makes a great noise. (A Swahili proverb)

18. The Light in the House

A STORY FROM THE GALLA PEOPLE

The People

At Lake Rudolf on the southern edge of Ethiopia, to the north of the tropic green of Africa's east coast, is a section of the Great Rift Valley. So deep is the Great Rift Valley that it seems as though an angry giant had split the mountains and the plains diagonally into two parts.

Ethiopia's people are divided also. They are as varied in origin as the Swahili. More than seventy different languages are spoken among the high mountains and on the hot deserts of Ethiopia. The official language is Amharic, spoken by the aristocracy. But it is generally less understood than the Galla language spoken by the tribes who poured westward into Ethiopia from the Horn of Africa many centuries ago. The tall, strong olive-skinned Gallas hoped that they would become the permanent rulers of this Christian kingdom, which was surrounded by Mos-

133

lem kingdoms and set like a vast island among almost impassable mountains. Today, although they account for half of Ethiopia's population and occupy part of the west, the south, and the east, the Galla people pay obeisance to Ethiopia's Christian emperor.

As keepers of camels and goats the majority of the Gallas live on the eastern plateau near the walled city of Harar. Turbaned Galla farmers, carrying long curved swords called *shotels* as protection against surprise attacks from bandits, pass along avenues of juniper and pepper trees when they bring their produce to Harar's markets. What pleasure they derive from the fruit trees and the fragrant herb and flower gardens set between the town's outer and inner walls! Perhaps they pick a ruby-red fig or a pomegranate to ease their parched throats if they have come across the desert lands.

A cacophony of sound draws the farmers beyond the second wall and into Harar itself. Open markets seethe with bustling traders who call raucously to the crowd to come buy their corn or sugar or sorghum or sheep or even horses. Barefoot boys, clothed in yards of cotton shawling, tend the camels and the donkeys when they are not milking goats or plucking plaintive music from a five-string *krar*, a kind of harp. Teen-age girls, sometimes with their hands colored with henna, offer silver bracelets and anklets or pins and earrings for sale. The jewelry, of delicate embossed silver or silver wire, is beautiful.

Of even greater beauty than the jewelry they wear, are the women who hurry through the narrow streets carrying baskets on their heads. Galla women love color. Shock-

135

ing-pink scarves are draped gracefully over electric-blue gowns that are, perhaps, embroidered finely in white flowers. A single string of gold drops on a chain of silver beads worn across their foreheads contrasts dramatically with the tribal markings that are tattooed on their cheeks and chins. A Galla woman's coiffure is her special pride. Tiny tight braids, no wider than a quarter of an inch, cover her head. An extra thin braid of about six hairs—no more—is pulled across her forehead. Painstakingly created, the arrangement is held in place with butter.

In spite of their many forward-looking ideas, some superstitions link the Gallas with a traditional past they are reluctant to discontinue entirely. When Harar's markets close at the end of each day and the traders load unsold merchandise upon their camels and lead them home, the city's scavengers poke around the empty stalls. They look for what hyenas consider delicacies. The practical Harar citizens actually feed the market leftovers to the hyenas, thereby cleaning up the town thoroughly. Should an albino hyena be one of the pack they call him "The White One." He is treated with respect, for Ethiopians believe that he is endowed with supernatural qualities, a reason perhaps why Hyena figures largely in Ethiopian stories.

The Story

Monkey was tired of his little house on the hilltop. He needed a change of scene so he decided to move to a new neighborhood in a shady valley near a grove of wild fig trees. Monkey devoted several hours each day to building a new round mud home with a grass roof. He left two openings in the wall for windows—one window faced the east, the other window faced the west. At the end of each day's work Monkey went back to his old home to sleep.

One night Hyena came slinking down the mountainside. When he saw the half-finished house he said to himself, "My, my! What a pretty house!" He carried on building the house where Monkey had left off.

Every day Monkey added to the building. Every night Hyena carried on the work. In no time at all the little house was finished and Monkey moved in.

Monkey brought in supplies of peanuts and walnuts and sticks of sugar cane and arranged them neatly on the pantry shelves. He unpacked a handsome new chair,

cut from a solid block of wood, and was about to relax before the fire when he heard a noise. A big animal was moving about in the bushes near the window that faced west. Monkey trembled. He heard the animal coming closer. Monkey fumbled with matches and lit a candle. Whatever it was crept closer. Monkey left the lighted candle and jumped out of the window that faced east. Better to live where I know my neighbors, he thought, than to be a monkey in some stranger's stewpot. He raced back to his old home and never came back.

And Hyena? What did he do? When Hyena saw the light he turned and slunk back to his mountaintop.

And the little new round house was left all alone forever—until it fell apart and sank into the ground.

19. Lion and the Woman

A STORY FROM THE AMHARA PEOPLE

The People

Ethiopian lakes, lively with waterbirds and reptiles, string through the Great Rift Valley where a high central plateau juts like a huge fortress beyond the valley's western wall. Among jumbled, rugged mountains and twisted gorges plantation owners find space for growing coffee and sugar, farmers for growing foodstuffs.

Addis Ababa, Ethiopia's capital, lies in a broad valley on the central plateau. Emperor Haile Selassie I reigns from a handsome palace facing a broad highway. The highway vibrates with the movement of people coming to conferences in Africa Hall, an imposing building across the highway from the royal palace. Diplomats come not only from distant parts of Ethiopia, but from all over Africa and the world beyond.

Ethiopians of Amharic descent, from whom come the

empire's rulers, predominate in the streets of Addis Ababa. Six hundred years ago they were converted to Christianity and the Coptic Christian faith is still Ethiopia's official religion.

Western-style dress is seen more and more in cosmopolitan Ethiopian cities. But Ethiopians living on the fringes of the cities and in the country wear their national costumes. If one were to meet a man of wealth and position on a country road he might be riding a white horse, adorned in velvet trappings and red-tasseled splendor. The man might be wearing white cotton jodhpurs under a long white tunic, a fine muslin *shamma,* a shawl, around his shoulders and over his head, and carrying a fly-whisk made from the white silky hair of a Colobus monkey. If the man meets a friend he dismounts, uncovers his head, bows, and shakes hands in the traditional salutation.

Formality attends every occasion. "Tenastilling," the traditional salutation, is extended a visitor to an Amharic Ethiopian's home before he enters the house, or *tukul.* Ethiopians usually build circular tukuls of clay and mud. They roof them with thatch and top them with ornamental clay spires. The house of a landowner is some-

times square to indicate his higher social status. Whether the house is round or square, it is sparsely furnished. A large round wicker table with chairs or stools occupies the center of the main living room. Around the table sit the diners who partake of the national dish which is *wat*, a highly spiced meat, served on large round pieces of *injera*, unleavened millet bread. The young people of a household do not sit at the table with their elders if they are under fifteen years of age.

The Amhara hostess wears an ankle length cotton gown, a *kamis*. She fastens a broad belt around her waist and covers her shoulders with a long, sheer shamma of hand-woven cotton. Women and girls who live in cities have adapted this style to modern needs. Their skirts, on which they sew strips of colored embroidery as trimming, are much shorter and fuller. They dress their hair in Western styles, and they wear shoes with heels.

Although young Ethiopian people do not eat with their parents at dinner time, they do join them in playing games after the meal. Perhaps one family member suggests *gebeta*, a game of skill in which two players maneuver beans on a gebeta board which has twelve sunken cups. If the boards are family heirlooms years of use have given them an ancient silken patina.

Until recently Ethiopians paid less attention to a girl's education than to a boy's. A girl helped her mother to weave and embroider, or to mold the great clay jars Ethiopians use for storing water. But as Ethiopia became less remote they recognized the value of education. Today, more and more girls as well as boys go to school.

Many boys consider making church work their careers when they reach high school age, for religion plays a large part in Ethiopian life. Boys who choose to attend church schools and to enter the priesthood must steel themselves for lives of tremendous austerity. They study Ge'ez, the Coptic ecclesiastic language, and they memorize the Psalms of David from the Bible. When the boys have mastered their assignments, they set out as wandering students, begging as they go. Their clothes are sheepskins, and they carry long staffs to ease their arduous journeys in difficult places. After the boys finish their education at advanced church schools, they may become either priests or teachers.

Educated boys and those who make religion their life work have little time to join their families for storytelling sessions. But when the violet light of evening comes after sundown and Ethiopian mountains take on an awesome beauty, then villagers delight in congregating to hear their favorite folktales.

The Story

There was once a woman who lived on a farm among Ethiopia's highest mountains. Although she was the wife of a rich man who gave her fine clothes and sparkling jewels, she was very unhappy. Her husband neglected her, sometimes staying away from home for weeks at a time.

The woman consulted the village wise man, saying to him, "My husband pays me little attention. Can you give me a charm, kind sir, that will bring him to my side again and thus end my loneliness?"

The wise man pulled his long cotton robe closer. He stroked his beard and thought deeply. Then he looked at the woman and in a kind voice said, "Yes, I can help you. But first you must pluck three hairs from a living lion's mane."

It seemed an impossible task. During her wakeful nights the woman heard Lion roaring in the ravine behind the farm, but she trembled at the thought of having to venture near such a frightening beast. Night after night she lay wondering what she could do to overcome her fear.

But the woman's wish to regain her lost happiness was stronger than her terror of Lion. One morning, just before daybreak, she mustered her courage and left her bed. She went to the farmyard. From among the new lambs she picked up her favorite. Cradling him in her arms, she followed the path that led into the ravine. She saw the fierce black-maned Lion. He stood quite still and glared at her.

The woman set the lamb down on the path. Then she turned quickly and went back home.

Every morning the woman went to the ravine at day-break. She always carried an offering of food. Lion came to expect the daily visit. One morning, when he approached her with his head held high and his tail wagging, the woman knew that she had won Lion's trust.

After that Lion ran to meet the woman every morning. He would rub his massive head back and forth against

her side while she stroked him gently and patiently. When she cleaned his matted mane of burs and thorns he purred like a kitten.

It was easy for the woman to pluck three hairs from her friend's neck. She carried them to the village wise man. "I have fulfilled your request," she announced triumphantly."

"Tell me all about it," the man said. He adjusted the hood that covered his head against the cold mountain breeze and prepared to listen.

The woman told him that by hiding her fears and using patience and understanding and affection she had made Lion her friend.

"Ah—" the wise man interrupted—"Patience! Affection! Use them and your wonderful understanding, my dear, and you will win back your husband. They are the charms I have to give you."

20. The Wise Old Camel

A STORY FROM THE EGYPTIAN PEOPLE

The People

In the old days, most of the people everywhere in Egypt were poor. Perhaps the poorest people were those who worked as sharecroppers on the estates in the Nile River delta that belonged to big landowners. Of a real necessity, even the children worked in the fields. The youngest children trod the water wheels—around and around and around. The little buckets that were attached to the huge wheels lifted the water and emptied it into channels leading to the thirsty cotton fields. The bigger boys and girls hoed or weeded or picked cotton all day long with the hot sun beating down on their thin, hungry bodies. The work was constant and left no time for schooling.

In 1952 revolution eased somewhat the cruel hard life for Egypt's peasants. The new government took the land

146

from the rich men and divided it among the poor. It cut broad canals from the Nile River, so that life-giving water flowed into the barren wastes. Where once there was desert, townships sprang up and flowers bloomed. And the people were made more independent and happier.

In one new town called Um-saybir (which means "patience"), families live on a cooperative, community basis. They live in neat white houses which—with electricity, water, and a Jersey cow for each—were gifts from the government. For privacy, high walls enclose the houses and their yards where goats and donkeys are stalled and chickens cooped. Contented coos come from dovecotes atop the walls, and dappled shadows fall from eucalyptus trees.

Every child in Um-saybir, as in each of the new towns, goes to school. And because the new town is a community project, some of the mothers assist as teachers. After school teen-age boys help their fathers grow beans and peanuts, clover, corn, and other vegetables on each family's allotted five acres of land. On weekends they play soccer and share in club activities. And boys and girls cooperate to stage short plays, which they have written, in the town's community hall.

Egyptian girls take to needlework and sewing as readily as they take to schoolwork. From an early age they stitch the colored cushion covers and other articles that beautify their homes. They bend over fine work such as hem-stitched lingerie—their large, long-lashed dark eyes intent on drawing threads or making an embroidered flower. Girls help to make the family's clothing with hand-woven

cloth from the towns' cooperatives. For stitching the long seams of the *galabiyah*—a long garment worn by both men and women—the family sewing machine is brought out. (A farmer and his family wear Western-style clothing when they visit a city.) While daughters sew, mothers bake the bread—large, dark, and flat—or prepare the main midday meal, which is usually rice, perhaps with sesame seeds added, and nuts. And for dessert, dates always take first place in popularity. Good relationships exist between mothers and their daughters. Lively talk, punctuated with jokes and laughter, lightens the work in Egyptian peasant kitchens.

The Nile delta, where the river separates into several streams, draws thousands of fish-eating birds that feed on the succulent morsels that hide in the marshy expanses. Nowhere is there a greater abundance of vigorous life concentrated. Tall graceful crested cranes, herons, and clumsy pelicans go about their business of poking in the reeds for frogs and snails, and for tiny fish and large worms. Egrets lazily ride the buffaloes and keep their hides free of cattle ticks. Crocodiles rob the birds' nests of eggs, and the Nile monitor, a large lizard, follows this bad example.

Life quickens in the delta with the arrival of migratory birds from Europe. Storks winter in Egypt. They arrive in an unbroken stream that darkens the sky for several hours before they land. The season's youngest storks, hatched and reared in northern countries, lead the flight while their parents follow. Storks feed mainly on locusts, which in their swarms devastate the land clear through to southern Africa. A campaign to exterminate Egyptian locusts is in progress, but it is feared by some people that if the locusts go, so will the storks.

An Egyptian family believes that when a stork chooses to live on their property good fortune will come to them. No wonder that Egyptian folktales include several that concern the storks.

The Story

Mrs. Stork was the most industrious bird in Egypt. Every fall as soon as she arrived she started making a vegetable garden. She collected seeds during her flight from the north, and these she planted first. Brussels sprouts and Swiss chard competed for size and greenness where they flourished in the rich black soil beside the Nile River. But it was really Mrs. Stork's knack for gardening that produced such flavorsome and appetizing results.

One fall Mrs. Stork planted her vegetables in a secluded spot completely surrounded by reeds and palms. Early every morning she flew down from her treetop house. She worked all day making things grow. Limas and other climbers twisted and curled around the poles that Mrs. Stork put out to support them. Peas and peppers, parsley and potatoes could have won prizes in horticultural shows for their tempting juiciness. Mrs. Stork loved her garden. She had hidden it where no one could find it. That's what Mrs. Stork thought. But Mrs. Stork was wrong.

Monkey, always curious, always poking into other

people's affairs, saw Mrs. Stork coming and going. He noted from the top of a date palm when the carrots and cabbages, the celery and the cucumbers were right for cutting. During the night Monkey beat a wide clear path through the reeds to the vegetable patch.

When Mrs. Stork arrived with her basket next morning she saw at once that a trespasser had been in her secret garden. She looked around uneasily. Then she saw Monkey behaving monkeyishly. He was sitting in the middle of the parsnip patch munching a melon.

"What are you doing in *my* garden?" Mrs. Stork squawked.

Monkey looked Mrs. Stork right in the eye. "What on earth do you mean? This is *my* garden. These are *my* vegetables. That is *my* path." Monkey casually pulled a radish, ate it, and shrugged.

"Stop eating *my* vegetables," Mrs. Stork screeched, shuddering at the cruel sight. "You're a bad monkey! Leave my garden! Go away at once!"

Monkey chattered and chittered, jumped up and down, trampled the parsley bed, and would not leave. Mrs. Stork clacked her bill and flapped her wings.

The noisy argument brought Donkey into the garden. He trotted in over monkey's path. "What's going on here?" he brayed.

"Monkey's ruining my garden. Please, make him stop. Make him go away." Mrs. Stork was becoming hysterical.

"This is *my* garden, Donkey." Monkey pointed. "See *my* path leading in. Day after day I've slaved to make things grow. Now she wants to take it from me."

151

"Seems to me it must be Monkey's garden," Donkey said, chewing on a carrot. "There's his path as clear as my long ears." But he was a terribly stupid donkey!

A deep voice came from the reed hedge. It was Camel. "What's all the fuss about?" he asked. "You're keeping the owls and the nightingales awake."

Monkey waved his arm. "Look, Camel, look! There's *my* path! This is *my* garden! I made it, but she wants to take it." He raced up and down smashing squashes and beating his chest.

Mrs. Stork dashed to Camel. "Please, Mr. Camel, make them stop spoiling the vegetables. Please, Mr. Camel, stop Monkey from prancing on the turnips. They're very frail." She fluttered from Donkey to Monkey. She fluttered back again. "Shoo! Go away! Please, Mr. Camel, make Donkey stop chomping the cauliflower. He's hurting them."

Now, Camel may have appeared stupid with his long-lashed eyes and his droopy dribbly mouth, but he was far from stupid! Camel was shrewd and clever. He saw through Monkey's faking and recognized Mrs. Stork's genuine agitation.

"Mmmm-mm-m-!" mumbled Camel in a ruminating manner. "It's as plain as the hump on my back whose garden *this* is."

Camel picked up Monkey with his big strong teeth. He tossed Monkey over the reeds and into the river with a splash. Camel shoved and pushed silly Donkey out along the path.

Mrs. Stork was tidying up when Camel came back. She straightened her ruffled feathers and gave him a birdlike

smile. "Oh, Mr. Camel," she cooed. "Thank you for saving my garden. I don't know what I would do if anything happened to my lovely plants. You are *so* clever and wise knowing that Monkey lied and cheated."

"Well—now, it's this way, Mrs. Stork. I always look a situation over ver-r-r-y carefully—not hastily, but carefully —before I pass judgment. That way I avoid making mistakes. This advice is good for everyone to follow. Don't you agree?"

Mrs. Stork agreed wholeheartedly as she filled her basket with luscious fresh vegetables. Mr. Camel helped her. Together they gave a delicious dinner party that night with the first crop from the garden.

The End of the Evening

Babies are sleeping, small children are yawning, only big children are wide awake when storytelling comes to an end in African villages. It is late. The storyteller stands up, stretches, looks up at the sparkling stars. They seem, somehow, to shine bigger and brighter in Africa than anywhere else in the world. They dangle in a tantalizing manner close to earth.

"See," the storyteller points to the sky. "It is time for all good children to gather the stars, to put them away safely in their own boxes until tomorrow."

So the children go to bed contented. They know that while asleep they will collect the stars and hide them where they will be safe through the daylight hours. This is one duty shared by all African children. When twilight falls the stars escape.

Night after night, year after year, this has been the pattern of life in villages all over Africa.

155

ABOUT THE AUTHOR

EDNA MASON KAULA began collecting tribal folktales on
her first trip to Africa in 1953. Since then she has spent many
years traveling in Africa and writing about the country and
the people. In this book she has assembled and retold the
best of the African folktales she learned from the village storytellers. Many of the tales were collected when she was gather-
ing information for a book she published in 1966 called
Leaders of the New Africa.

Mrs. Kaula has traveled extensively throughout the world
and has written and illustrated numerous books for adults and
young people. Born in Australia, she attended Sydney Tech-
nical College and later studied at art schools in Holland and
in New York, where she now lives.

1   2   3   4   5   72   71   70   69   68

398.2
K

Kaula, Edna Mason
African village folktales

A

Date Due

DEC 11	OCT 19	MAR 25	
JAN 19	NOV 8	APR 1	
MAR 29	DEC 7	JUN 1	
APR 30	FEB 6	MAY 7	
NOV 10	OCT 24	SEP 25	
JAN 20	NOV 13	FEB 22	
JAN 27	DEC 18		
FEB 18	FEB 12		
MAR 3	FEB 26		
MAR 23	MAR 25		
APR 26	WAGNER		

Authentic African tales from tribal storytellers, many of which are fables with a
moral.